LIFE AND WORK OF THE
NORTHERN LEAD MINER

LIFE AND WORK OF THE
NORTHERN LEAD MINER

ARTHUR RAISTRICK & ARTHUR ROBERTS

ALAN SUTTON

THE NORTH OF ENGLAND OPEN AIR MUSEUM

First published in UK in 1984

First published in the UK in this edition in 1990 by
Alan Sutton Publishing Limited · Phoenix Mill · Far Thrupp · Stroud · Gloucestershire

First published in the United States of America in 1991 by
Alan Sutton Publishing Inc. · Wolfeboro Falls · NH 03896-0848

British Library Cataloguing in Publication Data
Life and work of the northern lead miner.
  1. England. North Pennines. Lead mining industries, 1850–1930
  I. Raistrick, Arthur *1896–*   II. Roberts, Arthur *1938–*
  338.274409428

  ISBN 0–86299–826–3

Library of Congress Cataloging in Publication Data applied for

Typeset in 10/11 Garamond
Typesetting and origination by
Alan Sutton Publishing Limited
Printed in Great Britain by
Dotesios Printers Limited

INTRODUCTION

The purpose of this book is to illustrate the environment in which the northern lead miners lived and worked during the later years of the industry, approximately the second half of the nineteenth and the early decades of the twentieth century. This is made possible by the remarkable collection of material in the photographic archives of BEAMISH, The North of England Open Air Museum. In this archive, several hundred photographs relate to mines and miners, their homes and families, and their activities, in and out of the mines. The photographs extend in date from about 1850 to 1950, with the majority falling between 1860 and 1910. The area covered is the north Pennines, from Stainmore to the valley of the Tyne – that is the valleys of the Tees, Wear and Tyne, and their tributary valleys of Derwent, the East and West Allen, the Nent and the South Tyne. To fill some gaps, a few photographs from the western flank of the Cross Fell range, of Greenside Mine in the Lake District and a few from North Yorkshire have been included.

The majority of the Beamish photographs have been loaned, for copying, by the families and descendants of miners, without whose co-operation compilation of such an extensive archive would have been impossible. It would be impossible to name all the donors here, but all are acknowledged in the permanent archive at Beamish and a very genuine thanks is extended to them. R.H. Bird's 'Yesterday's Golcondas' and 'Britain's Old Metal Mines' may be consulted for other photographs of the area. H. Beadle's 'Mining and Smelting in Teesdale' (1980) provides an introduction to the Teesdale mines by one who has worked in them. More general history of mining in the area may be found in 'A History of Lead Mining in the Pennines' by Dr A. Raistrick and B. Jennings.

Lead mining is an ancient industry in this area, with some slight evidence of Roman mining in a few places and documentation for the thirteenth century, and later, available for most of the area. From the end of the seventeenth century, there are interesting contrasts and comparisons between the dominance of two large companies, the Blackett-Beaumont Company and the London Lead Company (more officially entitled the Governor and Company for Smelting Down Lead with Pit Coal and Sea Coal) and the numerous smaller groups and partnerships of miners scattered over all the area. In the later years of the nineteenth and first half of the twentieth century, the Weardale Lead Company and the Vieille Montagne Zinc Company succeeded to many of the Beaumont and London Lead Company leases. At the same time, however, there were small mines leased and worked by partnerships of a few men, selling their ore to the large companies or to the independent smelters. In the Yorkshire Dales, the Dukes of Devonshire and the Lords Wharton were, respectively, the largest mine owners in Wharfedale and Swaledale, from the late seventeenth century.

The smelting, which converted the mines' ores to merchantable lead, was done in the mills of the large companies or in mills erected by the royalty owners to smelt their duty lead, along with a number of small independent mills, most of which had only a short working life.

The activities in lead mining fall into four easily separated divisions – getting the ore, dressing it ready for smelting, and refining, which brings it to merchantable lead. The complexity of the carriage arrangements necessary for removing the waste materials, taking ore and fuel to the smelt mills and finished products to market form almost a subsidiary industry and make the fourth section. Power is needed throughout the industry, so

the provision of this will also be recorded. A brief note of some of the people and families who have been connected with the mines will make a final section which, if adequately dealt with, could be expanded to provide the material for another book.

Without the remarkable work done by Arthur Roberts, who was involved in making the collection of photographs, the skill employed in photographically copying prints, many of them old and faded, by the Museum staff, and the constant interest of Dr Frank Atkinson, Director of BEAMISH, The North of England Open Air Museum until 1987, this book could not have been made.

WORK IN THE MINE

Very little can be shown of the earliest mining which was almost confined to opencast: digging along a vein where it outcropped, leaving a trench which in almost all cases has been obliterated by later working. A few examples of later opencast working have survived but no exact date can be put upon them. An early development was the bell pit, whereby a row of shallow shafts was dug in succession along a vein. From the bottom of each, the vein was dug for a short distance, limited by the problems of ventilation and haulage. When a bell pit was abandoned it was filled with some of the debris from the next one in the succession. As with opencast, few bell pits have survived later working.

A method both of prospecting and working, which is almost unique to the steep-sided valleys of the Pennines, especially Swaledale, and to parts of Wales, is that of hushing. Water collected in a dam on the hill crest is released as a torrent which, tearing down the hillside, removes soil and weathered rock to reveal the underlying rock and any veins which may be in it. Repeated 'hushings' have in some cases produced ravines of large size. Hushing was more widely used as a method of getting ore. A vein cut by a hush would be repeatedly loosened with a pick and then washed out by a hush, the ore being sorted at the foot of the hush. This is the cause of the very large size of many hushes, some of which were still being worked in the 1890s.

A mine seen in the landscape has a number of necessary separate features, usually all present on a small mine, but on the mines of large companies, the dressing floors at the separate mines are usually replaced by a centralized dressing floor or mill.

The entrance to the mine is by level or shaft. Near the mouth, or portal, of the level, there is usually a building which often contained both the blacksmith's smithy and the miners' shop. The latter is a changing place and sometimes a lodging. At a place as near to the mine as is possible to find sufficient space and an abundant water supply, is the dressing floor which the larger companies may have replaced with a mill serving a group of mines. Deads, that is rock with no ore mostly cut from levels known as crosscuts, driven in 'dead' ground between veins, which could not be stowed underground, were taken to the dumps, or tips, near the level mouth. Ore and ore-bearing rock went to the bouse teams, or hoppers, on the dressing floor. Here, depending upon the size of the operation, there were varying amounts of machinery for performing the separation processes.

ACCESS TO THE MINE

The position of mineral veins having been discovered, the problem of access to them is largely determined by the topography.

It will be achieved either by sinking a shaft or by approaching the vein by a level. The north part of the Pennines offers a sharp contrast with the mid Pennines and Derbyshire. The main river valleys in the north Pennines from the Aire to the Tyne are roughly parallel, deep and generally have steep valleys which dissect the high ground. Almost all the mineral veins can be reached by levels driven from a low position in the valleys and intersecting them some hundreds of feet lower than general summit level. If properly designed, these levels are adits which drain all the workings above them and are also used to bring out the bouse without the lifting required when shafts are used. Some shafts will be sunk to promote ventilation and, in some cases, to pump water from workings below adit level. This contrasts with an area like Grassington Moor, in Wharfedale, which is remote from the river valley and so has no large working level, but a very large number of hoisting and access shafts, with an extensive system of dams and water courses to supply the centralized dressing floors and water wheels used for hoisting at the deeper shafts. So, the area that we are describing is characterized by many scores of levels and few of the miners would approach their work except by a longish walk through a level.

The dimensions of levels vary a little but they are generally around six feet high and three or four feet wide. Before the use of gunpowder was common, however, in rock – 'hard driving' – they would be kept as small as was serviceable. In shale and broken rock the excavation was made bigger to accommodate timber propping or stone arching. The London Lead Company introduced stone arching into its mines in 1818 and in 1827 it was ordered that 'all Drawing levels, Shafts and Sumps are now constructed of stone'. The portal was framed in well built masonry, commonly arched and sometimes with an inscribed or dated key stone. Stone arching or timbering was used until the level entered sound rock, or it might have been used right to vein where there was a complex of workings and the drawing of bouse was heavy. The London Lead Company was a most extensive user of stone arching at its Nenthead and other mines. The alternative was heavy timber framing, which was used where necessary throughout the working places. A report on the L.L.C. mines, in 1882, refers to 'the charges for winning stones and arching for its Teesdale mines, in the first quarter amounted to within a trifle of £600. This is a large sum to be expended every quarter in securing roofs of levels and on rises that give access to the roof workings but it is one of those mediums of expense that cannot be avoided and cannot be reduced without increasing the risk of injury to 'life and limb' of the miner, and of impeding the highway through which the products are sent to the surface.' The advantages were such that stone arching was adopted in many of the Blackett-Beaumont Mines.

The provision of timbering in mines was also a costly item. The simplest timbering called for large size (5 in diameter) timbers and bars, roughly cut to size and sent into the mine by staff working on the surface. The larger companies had their own woodyard, with saw mill and carpenters' shop, and a gang of 'wood cutters' who got the timber, often from the company's own plantations. Millwrights, or carpenters, operated in the saw mill and on the complex work needed for special jobs, such as fitting the huge rods for operating pumps in a shaft, or the ladderwork and framing in a shaft, ore chutes and so on. The men who did the main timbering underground and who co-operated in the special timbering were the timbermen, as much craftsmen as the carpenters. This group in the Weardale and Teesdale mines of the London Lead Company, numbered 47, and their wages for three months of 1882 came to nearly £600 and the carriage of wood added to that of timberwork was £787.

Iron rails were introduced in 1817 to replace wooden ones, and were laid in the levels. Some levels were called 'horse levels' where horses or ponies drew the tubs. A level usually had a slight inclination, a common amount being a rise of one inch in a few fathoms. This allowed water to run quietly, without erosion, and also a set of loaded tubs could be drawn out with an effort no more than that required to overcome the friction and irregularities of the track. The effort required to pull the empty set back into the mine was roughly equal to that of bringing out the full set, so the pony had nearly uniform work. The lowest level coming out to the day (the surface) was the main drain of the mines and thus always had a stream of water. If this was not too big it might be kept to a channel at one side but usually it occupied all the width of the adit. As the adit was the common entry to the mine, the miners were accustomed to arriving at their work place wet-shod unless their boots were exceptionally good. In the long adits, and they may sometimes be a mile or more long, the men would 'ride' in if possible. Either, a 'tram' was used which was a strong frame across which short planks were placed as temporary seats, or a special low sided timber tram was used. These trams were also used for carrying timber and other bulky materials into the mine.

Some of the horse levels were very long. Dunham quotes the following few examples in the Nenthead area: Hudgill Burn 13,350: Smallcleugh 22,430 and Capelcleugh 20,950 ft respectively. At a few mines where the level is of great length and a ventilation shaft has been sunk near to the working area, this shaft may be used also for 'riding' the men.

When the adit reaches the vein, the workings spread along it, taking out the ore and the minimum amount of 'deads' necessary to make working and travelling room. As most veins are nearly vertical, they are worked out upwards by a process known as stoping. As the stoping increases in height, a strong floor of big timber is put across it, above which the stope can be continued. A chute is built at one side, down which the ore is dropped into tubs in the drawing level. As the stope is worked upwards, the deads are left on the timbers to pile up as a working floor and, where necessary, more temporary timber is used for working places. In an old mine, these stope floors form the most serious danger. Half rotted and fungus-infected timbers may be holding scores of tons of partly wedged deads. A slight disturbance could bring this down into the level. The stope will be worked upwards only far enough to leave a supporting floor for the next level generally at a few fathoms interval. Levels at ten fathoms intervals are driven out from a shaft from the surface or rises are made from the level below. A connection sunk downwards from a working level is a winze. In some circumstances a stope is continued without intermediate levels and some reached great heights.

In the Northern Pennine ore deposits a common feature is the formation called flats. These are lateral extensions of the mineral from a vein along a bedding plane, either with deposition in cavernous areas or by metasomatic replacement of limestone. Working in flats is very different from vein stoping. The flat may be of considerable width and area and the height may also be so great that when worked it resembles a growing cavern. Here there is more space and air and the working is drier. There is considerable variation in the dimensions of flats. Sometimes, they are a broad-spreading, low, open area in a bedding plane of the limestone, lined with mineral. These are soon worked out, but may involve cutting barren rock to get sufficient working height. The most extensive and profitable are areas surrounding bedding planes where the rock is impregnated or in part replaced by ore. The proportion of ore in the rock is variable and flat ore usually calls for more careful dressing than good vein bouse. Amongst the largest flats are those of Rodderhope Fell, Rampgill, Allenheads and Boltsburn Mines.

A few special levels are driven in unusual circumstances,

drainage and/or exploration of a large area of ground being the general reason. There are two such examples in the North Pennine mining field, the Nent Force Level and the Blackett Level. About 1770, the Commissioners of Greenwich Hospital, who had held the Manor of Alston Moor from 1734, and its lessees, the London Lead Company, were studying two problems, that of draining the Nenthead Mines to make veins available in greater depth, and that of exploring the little known strata between Alston and Nenthead. Management of the estate was largely influenced by two 'receivers', Richard Walton, active in the area, and John Smeaton', adviser. In 1775, a scheme entitled 'A PLAN of the proposed LEVEL for unwatering the SILLS and discovery of all the VEINS . . . . Designed by Messrs Walton and Smeaton was made. It was proposed and accepted in February 1776, and it was resolved to start on the level at once. Commenced at 890 ft A.O.D. the level was to be 9 ft x 9 ft. but differences in the rock caused great variations in that section. Ventilation shafts were sunk at 7,200, 9,800, 13,325 and 18,125 ft from the portal, in which length the drive was to be level and have an average depth of five feet of water maintained in it, to act as a canal. At the end of this section, Haggs Shaft was used as a rise, and the upper part of the level started driving at 1,000 ft A.O.D. From here, the level rose at a gradient of nearly 1 in 100 to its end, near the Brewery Shaft, 28,090 ft from the portal and at 1,170 ft A.O.D. The drive took fifty years to complete but found few profitable veins.

The second of these long adits is the Blackett Level, in East Allendale. The Allenhead mines had proved to be very rich and, in 1855, the Blacketts decided, with their General Manager, Thomas Sopwith, to drive a long 'crosscut' level which would explore several miles of ground in East Allendale and on its completion, drain a great depth of ground below the Allenhead workings. The level was commenced from Allendale Town and three shafts sunk along its course, at Studden Dene, 5,300 ft from the portal; Holmes Linn, 11,958 ft and Sipton, 20,429 ft and 340 ft deep, to provide additional foreheads to expedite progress. It was intended to extend the level, which had opened up some very profitable veins, to the Gin Hill Shaft at Allenheads. From a point at the surface near the end of the Blackett level, the Fawside Level, another long crosscut, was driven to open up and serve the very rich area of the Allenhead mines.

CONDITIONS OF WORKING

In the earliest mining, before the invention of gunpowder, the miners' tools had been the pick, hammer, plug and feathers and crowbar. All of these tools remain in use to the present day, although the plug and feathers is seldom used. The two significant changes have been the introduction of explosives and the pneumatic drill. The use of some explosives created with their fumes large amounts of bad air and this increased the incidence of chest diseases. The use of the pneumatic drills, with their exhaust of large volumes of air, may have aided ventilation a little, and modern explosives reduced much of the danger from fumes.

In underground working of course, the first necessity is lighting. This, until surprisingly recent times, was provided by candles. At very small 'one man' (partnership) mines, candles were often 'home made' from any fats or tallow that could be collected. On a large mine, the candles were bought by contract and sold to the men, the cost of candles being a large item in the accounts of any mine. Even at a small mine like Langden Head, the charge on four weeks to John Teward and his son was 30s for candles and 26s for powder. Some indication of cost can be gained for the Alston Moor Mines of the London Lead Company, when

the Court recorded, in 1815, that purchasing candles by competition had saved £225 in that year.

The candle was usually carried in a simple lamp, a tin with one side cut out and a hole in the bottom through which the candle could be fed. A handle of some kind was added for ease of carrying. A bunch of spare candles was usually taken into the mine. Even a home-made lamp of this kind saved the candle flame from loss by guttering in the draughts of levels and drives.

The first great improvement was the acetylene lamp which, when filled with carbide and water, would give an intense white flame for the whole of the shift. While travelling through the levels it was not as easily blown out as a candle. It could be hung up at the work place and gave a good and steady light. A further improvement was the electric cap lamp, which concentrated the light on the actual work and so cast no shadows on it. Travelling the levels it left the hands free, an advantage on ladders in the rises. The carbide lamp had only a limited capacity of carbide and so would need recharging in a long spell of work. The electric lamp, with a re-chargeable battery carried in a pocket or on a belt, was the latest improvement still in general use. Before these improvements, the eye trouble called 'miners' nystagmus' was a common affliction of the older workers.

One of the most prevalent disabilities of miners until the mid-twentieth century was chest trouble. This was a consequence of dust, damp, fumes of explosives and foul air, aggravated by poor ventilation. Asthma, bronchitis and pneumoconiosis all contribute in varying degree, but few miners can escape all of them. After 1882, tuberculosis was recognised as a result or accompaniment of lung damage. The problem of ventilation is one that affects every mine and to secure good air many expedients have been tried. The problem arises early in the opening of a mine, as the level for access is driven with a dead end and gets steadily further from fresh air. For short levels, bellows at the entrance or sometimes at the working end, were used. Large bellows could be horse driven with pipes used to convey the air to the forehead. In 1737, the London Lead Company was driving two adits at the Shilden Jeffreys mines and its accounts include many items such as 'Shildon Dec. 1737, 50 yards of air pipes @ 20d', and 'Jeffreys June 1738, levell; putting air pipes and drawing water.'

More common was the 'windy billie', a small hand blower which a boy would operate near the working place. This did little more than keep the air stirring.

The aim of an efficient ventilation system was to create a draught through as much of the mine as possible and so improve working conditions. In driving a long level, this could be done by sinking a shaft onto it from the surface. Both the Nent Force and the Blackett Levels have such shafts at intervals along their length, sunk to promote ventilation and with some of them only later used for drawing. On the Nent Force Level, the first shaft was Watergreens at 7,200 ft from the portal. This was the longest interval to a shaft and this was achieved with the aid of a water blast near the portal, which provided air for the first section. The other shafts were Foreshield, 2,600 ft further; Lovelady Shield, 3,525 ft; Haggs, 4,800 ft; Wellgill, 4,500 ft and Brewery, 3,465 ft further and practically at the end of the level. The driving of pilot tunnels went on from the bottom of the shafts to secure, as quickly as possible, a through connection for ventilation. These could then be enlarged to finished size. On the Blackett Level, the shafts were Studden Dene, Holmes Linn and Sipton. The lengths of the two levels are respectively 4.94 and 4.5 miles.

Another way of securing ventilation in a level was to make a timber floor just above the rock sole, and air would be drawn in through this space as warm exhausted air escaped along the roof. The water blast was widely used in the north, and is mentioned in

1730 as being in use in the Blackett-Beaumont Mines. In 1831, a visitor (Turner, *Trans. Newcastle Lit. & Phil. Soc. Vol.1, 1831*) describes in detail the water blast at Allenheads. A report on the London Lead Company's mines, in 1864, says that the common practice was to have a water blast on every new long level. The principle is simple; water falling through a pipe down a shaft takes with it air drawn through snore holes at the top. This is trapped in a receiver at the bottom and drawn off at the pressure of the head of water and in some cases, the air was driven along the trunking by a fan driven by the force of the escaping water. The water blast at Brewery Shaft was replaced by the Vieille Montagne Company, which installed Pelton Wheels to drive air compressors for rock drills.

Most of these efforts improved conditions in the levels and the main part of the mine but, during the period to which most of the illustrations belong, few of the men escaped some onset of chest or eye trouble. this was only partly countered by the widespread custom, encouraged and assisted by the larger companies, of the men having allotments or in many cases small holdings. The work on these, exercise in fresh air, and the fresh vegetables and milk got from them, were a great help towards better health.

GETTING ORE

The greatest change in working methods, which marks the beginning of modern mining was that made by the introduction of explosives for breaking the rock. This involved drilling many more holes, with a consequent increase in dust. The change from gunpowder to dynamite, in the 1870s, also added more toxic fumes.

The invention of the compressed air drill reduced the labour and introduced additional air into the working end from the exhaust. The early use of dry drilling, however, resulted in a massive increase in dust emission, much of which was finer than that produced by hand drills, thus aggravating the chest ailments. This was alleviated by the addition of a water jet to the drill bit, which both slaked the dust and flushed the hole whilst drilling. It is also likely that the increase in frequency of blasting produced even more dust and fumes, to an extent more deleterious than any gain from air brought in by the drills. Compressed air was provided in many larger mines by compressors in underground engine rooms, driven by electricity or by water power.

A key man was the shot firer who had to charge the holes, which had been drilled to a particular pattern set out according to the nature of the rock and what the shot was designed to bring down. So long as black powder was used it was issued regularly to the miners, but the shot firer was set on specifically to handle dynamite and subsequent cartridge explosives. He set the explosives in the drill holes, fitted them with fuse, or wired them with detonators for electric firing and stemmed them with inert packing to prevent them blowing out. When the men were drawn away to a safe place, he fired the shots, was responsible for knowing that all the holes had gone off and that it was safe for the men to return and remove the broken rock and resume drilling.

The broken rock and ore was taken to the nearest level or chute and from there it was taken out of the mine by 'drawers'. As much as possible of the deads were stowed in the mine. Some was built into packs to strengthen level walls, while some was left piled on timbers in the stopes.

A stope is made on the width of vein working. At a convenient height, a heavy timber floor is made with a chute at one side to deliver bouse into a waggon. Above this, the working is continued upward, and bouse is dropped down the chute with deads piled on the floor. Stoping is continued upward as long as possible from the top of the growing heap of deads, until another floor is necessary, the chute and the ladderway being extended to the next stage. Stoping thus leaves a number of timber stages loaded with many tons of deads, and liable to weakening by fungus and decay. Stopes of this kind make one of the very serious dangers in old mine workings.

The bulk of rock excavated to make working room will always far exceed the bulk of bouse so, in addition to stowage in the stopes and in abandoned workings, there is always the labour and expense of carriage onto the tips near the level mouth or the shaft top.

In early mining, the miners moved the deads as best they could. They were probably dragged along the levels in leather bags or on sledges, some of which have been found. Wheeled tubs were introduced in the sixteenth century and after this, the separate job of 'drawing' became recognized. In a small partnership it was common practice for one man or a boy to take the responsibility of tramming out bouse to the bouse team and deads to the dump. This would only take up part of his time in a small mine and he would fill in with work in the mine. A single tub, which was of massive construction, would be used and it was loaded and emptied by the trammer. Wheel-barrows were often utilized in flats, and were run on planks, laid along the deads to the nearest hopper. The drawing in a larger mine, until well into this century, and in some mines nearly up to the present time, was done by ponies. Even a small mine might have a pony to do its drawing, along with all its general carting.

In a large mine, drawing was a much bigger and heavier job. Bouse and deads were brought out in 'shifts' of six or eight tubs, a horse rather than a pony being used. Good organizing and timing was necessary as a level used for tramming might also be the waygate for a large number of men. The horse level, particularly the large sectioned stone-arched levels of the London Lead Company eased many difficulties of the movement of a shift of tubs and the chutes assisted the loading. On this scale, the drawing was separated from ore getting and was a separate job let by contract by the owning company.

Contracting, however, encountered difficulties. For a time, the Agents were allowed to organize the drawing and to own and keep horses with the company supplying the tubs. In the London Lead Company this was challenged and the drawing contract was let by outside tender between 1785 and 1815. Again there were abuses and the company took it over completely, with its own horses and horsemen, noting in the next year that in Teesdale the saving had been £521 and in 1818 in Alston Moor, £350. The introduction of iron rails to replace the oak ones in 1821 saved a further £250. This system continued until 1843 when some mines reverted to outside tender and this mixed method continued for much of the succeeding time until it was replaced by mechanical traction in a few of the larger mines.

Drawing usually included both filling and emptying the waggons but sometimes an emptier was employed where many different partnerships were at work in the mine and their bouse had to be kept separate in different compartments of the bouse teams.

We have already mentioned shafts sunk to promote the ventilation of a mine. As these were usually sunk as near as possible to the working complex, it was logical that in many cases they could be used to hoist deads and bouse to the surface, substituting overground carriage of bouse to the dressing floors, for the underground haulages. This could be by road, aerial ropeway, or by light railway, all methods being found, varying with the topography and other factors. At some of the more modern mines, where shafts were convenient and the walk to them easier than by a long level, they also wound men.

During the war, and in the post-war years, the huge dumps left, especially at the nineteenth-century mines, have proved to be profitable if their content is subjected to the modern separation methods which were not available to the 'old man'. Some of the largest tips at Nenthead have now been rewashed and replaced by smaller ones coming as refuse from the new mill. The same has happened in Weardale, where mills on a larger scale than any earlier ones have been erected to deal not only with bouse from re-opened mines, but with what was formerly rejected as deads. The quantities involved are such that a slight percentage difference in efficiency of treatment gives old dressing residues almost the status of mine bouse. The old dead heaps also contain a useful percentage of minerals like barite and fluorite, rejected by the earlier miners, but now in great demand.

WORK ABOVE GROUND

Ore Dressing or Washing

Bouse as delivered from the mine had been separated from the obvious large pieces of rock which were, when possible, retained in the mine for packing, and the smaller deads either stowed in stopes or trammed out to the dead heaps. Bouse – anything containing ore, much or little – was the raw material for the dressing floor and was brought out to the row of bouse teams. These were numerous enough to provide for the bouse of different partnerships to be kept separate so that it could be dressed and paid for separately. If the bouse was very lumpy it might be taken from the team to be picked over or carried to the knockstone, where boys or women used a spalling hammer to break off obvious pieces of stone, or a bucker to break it down to a gravel size suitable for either stamps, introduced to the Nenthead Mines in 1796, or roller crushers. The rollers had been introduced from South Wales in 1820 but stamps were still used occasionally to provide a second fine crushing in the dressing process. At some mines, jaw crushers were used in the early stage of preparation.

When the bouse had been reduced to a small uniform size, fine gravel or sand, it was then subjected to several processes of washing, all designed to get rid of spars and stone, leaving clean concentrate or smitham (or smiddam), which, though never one hundred percent ore, was suitable for smelting. The aim of the dressing was to get as high a concentrate as possible. The basis of the washing processes was the great difference in specific gravity of the ores compared with the spars and stone: for instance, while the specific gravity of pure galena is 7.75, that of fluorspar is only 3.2; calcite 2.6; barytes 4.5; and limestone about 2.6.

A stream of water can be arranged strong enough to carry away the spars and rock but not enough to take the ore. Nearly all dressing, except modern chemical processes and those using surface tension in special liquids, as in froth flotation and other scientific refinements, depended on the application of moving water. For a good separation it was essential that all the material should be reduced to particles of identical size and before the introduction of the roller crusher this was very difficult to attain with hand sieves, as these could not deal with the large quantities to be handled. After the hand picking, the crushing rollers would deal with the produce of several small mines or one large one at a dressing mill. Power to drive the rollers was provided by a water wheel and a surviving example is seen at the fine mill at Killhope in Weardale, set up in 1828. Unfortunately, the rollers and all the machinery have been removed in this century, partly for scrap but partly for re-use at another mine. The first crushing at Killhope was followed by a set of trommels which was the general practice by the mid-nineteenth century. The trommels were a succession of cylindrical sieves mounted on one axis, rotating and

set at a slope so that the bouse would move down inside them. The sections, four or more, started with the finest perforations and each succeeding section had larger perforations, so that the bouse was separated into even-sized lots. At the Killhope Mill, the trommel perforations were 1/16, 1/8, 1/4, 3/8, 1/2 and 5/8 of an inch. Whatever bouse failed to pass through any of these was passed to a further set of rollers and thence returned to the trommels. The fines from the 1/16 and 1/8 section were taken to the first wet process, the buddles, but the remaining four separations each went to a hotching tub or jig, the trommels and jigs occupying the mill along with the second, smaller crusher.

The hotching tub was a mechanized version of the age-old hand sieve. If finely crushed bouse on a sieve was jerked up and down in water, the rush of water through the sieve lifted and agitated it and, in settling, the much heavier ore would settle more quickly than mixed pieces or pure spar and with skillful manipulation the final result was bouse arranged in gradation on the sieve and the finest particles going through the sieve and similarly layered in the bottom of the tub. Sieving in a quiet stream had been in use from before the sixteenth century and was soon transferred to a tub where the fines which went through the sieve were saved. About 1810, Captain Barratt at the Grassington Moor Mines hung the sieve on the end of a lever which supported it in a tub, so making it easier for a man or a boy to operate a much larger sieve more efficiently. This was the hotching tub, soon adopted everywhere.

The hotching tub or jig was the most important machine on the dressing floor and so was soon the subject of improvements. One hotching tub could treat from 8 to 15 tons of bouse a day. At Allenheads, the tubs were improved by suspending the sieve by rods from levers which had a counterbalance weight at the other end. The levers could be jerked easily by boys. In what were generally called jigs, the sieves were suspended from eccentrics on a rotating power driven shaft.

A revolutionary change was made, not in principle, but in its mechanical application, by Petherick, in Cornwall, in 1831. This hotching tub had two connected compartments, often the two limbs of a U. The sieve was fixed in one and in the other a piston moved up and down, pulsating the water through the sieve. This variety was adopted at Allenheads, Nenthead and many of the larger dressing floors. The hand operated hotching tub remained the chief tool on the dressing floor of most small mines.

At nearly every stage of the washing some of the finest ore, produced because of the great brittleness of galena, was carried off in the wash water, so settling tanks, called trunks were used. In these a slight separation could be got by constant stirring. This was a job for boys, or on some floors it was done by a small water wheel driving mechanical stirrers. The sludge from the trunks which followed hotching, and which was called slimes was treated on improved buddles. The simplest buddle had been a slightly inclined trough with a stream of water running down it. Slimes or, in the earlier days, finely ground ore, was put onto the buddle and constantly moved up with a long handled shovel against the stream. Riffles or even turfs on the bottom served to catch the ore while the lighter spars, stone and clay were washed away. This was the straight buddle often used as the principal dressing method after the hotching tub on small mines.

A widely used mechanical adaptation was the circular buddle. This was a circular trough about 20 ft diameter and 2 ft deep and sloping outward from a central boss which varied in its height and diameter, as did all details within narrow limits according to the ideas of the managers at different dressing floors. In operating the circular buddle the slimes were fed as a liquid slurry to the centre and distributed over the central boss to run evenly over the very low cone of the floor. The even distribution was helped by two revolving arms carrying brushes which swept the slurry round the buddle. The heavy ore was dropped first against the centre boss, the spars and deads were carried towards the perimeter and between these two zones the middles or chats were dropped; material which still carried some small amount of intermixed ore. When the buddle was filled to a depth of about 20 in. these three zones were dug out separately. The inner one to about 3 or 4 ft wide, the heads, is enriched to about 40 per cent ore, and when treated a second time can produce a concentrate of 70 to 75 per cent. The middle or chats may hold as much as 10 or 12 per cent of ore and are returned to the buddles but the outer zone of deads go to the waste heap. A buddle can treat about 2 tons an hour of the material from the sludge trunks which follow the hotching or jigs.

In the second half of the nineteenth century many improvements to the buddle were made though most of them were modifications of single features. One which was quickly adopted was to replace the brushes which revolved and swept the water over the surface, by four arms which were perforated pipes, revolving and delivering water in sprays evenly on to the surface. Many changes were made in the dimensions and slopes of the central boss, and some in the feed of slurry to the buddle.

There was one introduction which was adopted in the North by the London Lead Company and a few other mines. It was generally known as the impeller or Lisburn buddle. In principle this returned to the most primitive method, the agitation of bouse in a running stream of water. Four rods about six feet long were mounted horizontally between two circular frames or wheels which rotated. A series of small metal plates or scrapers were mounted along the rods and turned at an angle to the length to make spirals round the frame. This was fixed above a casing, part of a cylinder, so that the scrapers revolved within a small distance of it. On one side this basal cylinder was continued by a rising slope down which water ran and spread over its whole width. At the other side the cylindrical part was followed by a wide flat which sloped slightly. The fine material was fed into the cylinder at one end and the blades of the rotor picked it up in the quick stream of water and by their spiral arrangement kept it moving through the stream which washed the lighter stuff away. The ore and chat were carried along in the axis direction to the other end where it was ejected into a tank. This true buddle action was automatic and continuous and the first concentration was about 40 per cent. Waste which had been carried away by the stream was caught on the flat and given a second treatment. The effective concentration achieved with most bouse by the whole process was about 70 per cent.

In 1849 Attwood introduced on some of the London Lead Company's floors a modification consisting of three trunking buddles where the bouse was kept moving by a paddle wheel. All that remains of any of these are the three long troughs at one or two mines. The finest slimes from these were treated in a dolly tub.

From the buddles some very fine material escaped with the overflow and draw-off water into the slime pits or settling tanks which also received slimes from other apparatus. These slimes could either be re-treated on buddles or on an Allendale invention, the Brunton Cloth, which was widely used on the larger dressing floors. It was essentially a mechanized straight buddle. It was a continuous wide belt of strong coarse canvas stretched between two rollers, one higher than the other to incline the cloth along its length. It was strengthened by slats at intervals across it which kept it flat and served as riffles. The underside was slack and dipped into a tank of water. The cloth was moved up the slope at about 15 ft a minute and had a stream of water running down it. The mud from the slime pits was thrown onto the cloth

about a third way down its length. The velocity of the water was sufficient to carry away the light waste while grains of ore settled on the cloth and were carried over and washed off in the tank. This enriched the slime to about 45 per cent concentrate and this went to final treatment in dolly tubs.

Joseph Stagg, of the London Lead Company, in 1828, introduced an entirely new machine into the process of dressing. This was a table suspended by four chains so as to slope gently towards one corner. Over it water flowed in a continuous sheet. It was connected by a crank to a power source which jerked the table regularly and in quick repetition. Slimes were fed in at the top and the combination of running water and the jerks separated ores and spars into separate bands. By the twentieth century the table in many forms had become an essential part of the modern mill. One later form of table was made circular, rotating on a vertical axis.

With the coming of the Vieille Montagne Zinc Company, in 1896, new and modern mills were built at Nenthead and at Rodderhope, where jigs and tables of developed forms were in operation. To meet the demands of the war years of the first part of the present century the larger companies, Beaumont, Vieille Montagne, Weardale Lead and others who followed them, built new dressing mills with new machinery and new power sources entirely superseding the open air dressing floors. Sipton, in East Allendale, is an example of a 'new' mine with a deep shaft and new mill, though the Blackett Level shaft top and remains of the old water wheel both remain on the site.

The Vieille Montagne Zinc Co demolished the existing mill buildings at Nenthead village and erected a new plant on the site with a complete run through from the roughest bouse to fine concentrates. After 1919, this mill was idle for most of the 1920s and was refurbished when Wellhope Shaft was sunk, although only working for a few months at this time. During the 1939–45 war, the mill was taken over by the Government and more modern ancillary equipment was added. Again, this mill only worked for a short period before the end of the war. The mill was subsequently taken over by the Anglo-Austral Company and used to process ores, including fluorspar, from the Northern Pennines area. Its final period of working was under a local concern known as Rampgill Mill Ltd, which was mainly involved in the processing of old dumps. In the period up to about 1919, the mill had taken ore from the mines in the valley south of Nenthead and also received ore from the West Allendale mines via connected mine workings. An aerial ropeway was built to connect it with the Wellhope Shaft, but this was a technical failure and was rarely used. The Vieille Montagne Zinc Company also erected a second entirely new mill, on the site of the old dressing floors at Rodderhope Fell Mine. At various times, this also took ores from Haggs Mine until a mill was built there following the failure of the ropeway to the mill at Nenthead.

Before the building of the mills, work on the dressing floors was both heavy and exposed to all the severity of the weather. With the quantity of water used it was impossible to keep dry with the clothing then available. Frost often cut off the water supply and a dreary — and often ineffective — time was spent breaking ice on the water courses on high and exposed moors. Some of the larger companies were able to find jobs for boys in the mine while frozen out from the dressing floors.

It is not possible, nor would it be profitable, to attempt a comparison of the hardships of work underground and on the dressing floors. Where underground health was undermined by bad air, dust, fumes and general over-exertion in a poor atmosphere and insufficient light, the dressing floors were fully exposed in large part to the weather and nearly all the work was concerned with moving water and the movement of materials in and out of water. It was practically impossible for a dresser to keep himself dry and warm and conditions often became intolerable. The photographs presented here show the transition period when the open dressing floors were being supplied with sheds and closed buildings, necessary to protect the machinery being introduced. Boys, men and women could be exposed to the weather, and replaced if their health broke down, but a machine was too valuable for such exposure. Advancing technology in the twentieth century has brought the large scale mill enclosing all stages necessary for the dressing of ores.

Smelting

Separate from the mine there is the smelt mill which usually served a group of mines from which the dressed ore was brought as concentrates or smitham. The location of the smelt mill was determined by different factors from those of the mine which is determined by the position of the veins and the topography in which they occur. The smelt mill must have reliable power to work its furnace bellows, access to fuel supplies and a convenient site in relation to the transport of ore from the mines to the mill, and for the finished lead from the mill to be carried to markets or to depots from which it can be despatched to or collected by customers. The first and foremost consideration is the necessary blast which is provided by a reliable stream and bellows for ore hearths, or a hillside flue and chimney for reverberatory furnaces; so the mills will be sited in the lower part of valleys.

When the bouse from the mine has been brought by dressing to a concentrate of 70 per cent or more of ore it is sent to the smelt mill where the metallic lead is extracted and refined into a merchantable form. In early days this was done in open, winds blown fires, some traces of which, as bail hills or boles, are found on most hillsides of the mining area. In Weardale, bellows were used at a few footblasts as early as the fifteenth century. These were followed by a small blast furnace and then there was developed the ore hearth which remained the principal means of smelting in the Northern mining field right into the present century. In 1745 the London Lead Company rebuilt the smelt mill at Nenthead with ore hearths of an improved type. Other improvements were made by Robert Stagg in the course of his work. This improved hearth was rapidly brought into use at all the smelt mills in the North. The hearth was simple, very like a blacksmith's hearth but with a deep bowl to hold a quantity of molten lead. The tuyer was at the centre at the back just above the bowl. At the front edge was the work stone on to which partly smelted bouse (aggregated lumps of partly smelted ore and slag) could be drawn to be examined and replaced in an appropriate part of the fire. The workstone is the full width of the hearth and is gently inclined with a groove across it down which the molten lead which collects in the hearth can overflow into a sumpter pot, from which it can be ladled into pig moulds for casting. The slag also runs off but is trapped in a mass of cinders partly filling the pot, the heavier molten and more fluid lead sinking through the cinders. Some of the slag is stiffened in the hearth by the addition of lime and can be picked out by the smelter and thrown to one side. In some advanced hearths much of the slag can be run off and carried away. The sumpter pot has a small fire under it to keep the lead liquid enough for casting.

From lighting up to the end of the smelt takes about ten to fifteen hours and will produce about 1 ton of metal. The regulation of the blast by regulation of the water wheel is an essential part of the smelters' skill. As the molten lead accumulates the smelter ladles it out into the cast iron moulds to make pigs, which have the name of the mill or the company on the base. Ores can vary in composition and the smelted lead may contain substances which

alter its quality. Small quantities of antimony make it brittle and unsuitable for making into sheet or pipe work. All lead ores contain silver which may be several ounces per ton in the smelted lead. This again will affect the properties of the lead and also may be worth extracting for its own value. Most of the lead is therefore refined to make 'merchantable' quality. This is done in a refining furnace (usually a reverberatory) or in special apparatus for the recovery of silver. The slag from the ore hearth still contains some lead and much of this can be recovered by re-smelting in a slag hearth. This is a short blast furnace, not much different in size from an ore hearth, but using coke as its fuel with a strong, steady blast. The slag from this furnace is black and vitreous, easily distinguished from the 'grey slag' of the ore hearth.

As ores from different veins often vary in composition and the processes of smelting and refining need careful checking, the larger smelt mills employed an assayer and maintained a laboratory and the processes and products were tested and constantly regulated. The London Lead Company had their assayers trained by the Professor of Chemistry at Durham University.

To reduce the danger from fumes, most smelt mills were airy places with open arches, or with wide louvres, opposite the hearths. The smelters thus had the heat of the hearth on their faces and the cold draught on the backs of their necks. To counter this in some mills it was customary for the smelters to wear thick knitted shawls round neck and shoulders when working at the hearth.

The recovery of silver from the smelted lead had been accomplished, from Roman times, by cupellation. The lead was re-melted in a blast of air which oxidized the lead to litharge but did not oxidize the silver. This was done on a bed of bone ash into which the litharge was absorbed leaving the silver in a small cake on the surface. The 'test bottom', as the bed of bone ash containing litharge was called, was re-smelted to reduce the litharge and recover refined lead. A revolutionary change was made in 1833 by Hugh Lee Pattinson, born in Alston in 1796, who after a time as assay master at the Langley Mill of the Greenwich Hospital moved to the Beaumont Mill at Blaydon. By his process lead was melted in a series of set-pans each kept at a critical temperature by a small fire. On cooling slowly crystals of lead begin to form in the liquid metal, which Pattinson found were poorer in silver than the original melt. By moving these to the next pan, and repeating the process several times in a series of pans the remaining liquid melt became greatly enriched in silver and most of the lead was desilvered. The lead crystals are ladled down the row of pans with perforated ladles and the greatly enriched silver-lead alloy left in the last pans was re-melted and silver separated in the refining furnace. The London Lead Company purchased the patent in 1836 after trial and perfection at Nenthead Mill. It was adopted by them at their mills at Stanhope, Bollihope, and Eggleston as well as at Nenthead.

In time other methods of silver recovery were discovered one of which, patented in the 1870s by Rozan used jets of steam to stir the molten lead. He used two large pots holding up to 30 tons or more and drained the enriched lead away leaving the desilverised crystals in the pot. By this method there was much mechanization with a marked saving of labour. A report in 1882 says that Rozan plants were then in use at Nenthead, Egglestone and Stanhope mills. Unfortunately, no photographs seem to have survived of the Rozan plant. When the smelt mills were demolished the sumpter pots and Pattinson pans were re-used as water troughs or broken up for scrap.

As lead is fairly volatile at smelting temperatures there was always a serious risk to the health of the smelter as well as undesirable damage to vegetation around the smelt mill. The heavy fumes settling in the immediate neighbourhood of the mill poisoned the vegetation which in turn poisoned sheep and cattle which grazed on it. This ground was called 'belland ground'. In 1778 Bishop Watson published the suggestion that a long flue on the ground between the furnaces and chimney on a nearby hill would cause the lead fumes to condense and not only make the smoke largely innocuous but would save a valuable amount of recoverable lead. These flues were adopted at once at the London Lead Company's Derbyshire mills and very soon after at their northern mills. Within a short while, flues were introduced to the Blackett-Beaumont Company's mills and at the Langley and Gaunless mills.

All the chimneys except the ones at Nenthead, Langley, Allen and Gaunless have now been felled but much of their flues remain. The flues are of considerable length – the Allendale flues are 12,213 yds long. The expense of maintaining the flues led to the invention of various types of condenser chambers. These were mostly added to the flues to cope with smelt mill extensions or to increase the flue efficiency.

The first of them was made by Stagg in 1843 in which the smoke was drawn through water, but Stokoe a little later made one which was a chamber filled with brushwood over which water was falling and through which the fume was drawn or impelled by a fan. Several modifications were made but all were additions to improve the efficiency of the flues.

Besides desilverisation, other impurities had to be removed from lead before it was of marketable quality and this was done in a refining furnace, often a reverberatory. A large smelt mill therefore required many buildings for different processes and often had offices and a house associated with it, so that Sopwith could describe the Langley Mills as having the appearance of a small village. Something of this complexity can be seen in the ruins of several of them. Langley Mill in 1767 had buildings to accommodate 3 ore hearths, 1 slag hearth, 2 refining furnaces, 1 reducing furnace and 1 roasting furnace. Other buildings were fuel houses, bone ash house, stables and a residence for the head smelter. Besides all these there were a number of cottages to accommodate the smelters.

In addition to the many buildings there were yards among them adapted to specific purposes. Near the building housing the ore hearths there was a range of bouse teams to keep apart ore from various sources ready for smelting. There was a fuel yard with coal bunkers and a peat house necessary to store a large quantity as getting peat was confined to one short season of the year. In a yard near the refinery the pigs of finished lead were stacked, and sometimes the workshops of various crafts, blacksmiths and carpenters, would find their place near the smelt mill complex. Checking, weighing and dispatching lead, looking after the ore, fuel and other stores demanded office staff and buildings so that a principal smelt mill involved a small community of many skills.

An essential part of a smelt mill were the bellows which provided the blast for ore hearths and blast hearths. Only the reverberatory furnace could operate on the draught provided by a high chimney supplemented by long flue. A water wheel was the motive power for the bellows, and an important part of the buildings was the accommodation for the bellows which took up more space than the furnaces. This can be seen in the plan of the Langley Smelt Mill.

The supply of fuel was a very essential service for the smelt mills. The North Pennines were fortunate in their geology for this. The Millstone Grit which capped most of the fells had some good coal seams near its base and there were also a few usable seams in the upper Yoredale Series. The fells were also blanketed by peat often many feet thick. In the earlier centuries the smelting was done with peat and wood but by the eighteenth

century the ore hearths were using a mixture of peat and coal and the reverberatory furnace used only coal.

The peat cutting was in part made a family occasion for the domestic supplies. Everyone could help, women and children setting up the peats in windrows for drying, later serving the men building stacks, and eventually helping with the loading for final carriage. This was also the case in peat getting for mills when wives and older children could earn a small wage.

The various smelt mills were served by small collieries not far away. In 1704, and to its end, the Whitfield Smelt Mill, of the London Lead Company, used coal from Coanwood Colliery. The Langley and Allen Mills depended upon nearby Stublick Colliery. This colliery was in a patch of Lower Coal Measures brought down by the Great Stublick Dyke (Fault) which dominates the Tyne Valley. Many of the Weardale smelt mills depended on coal from Grey Mare Collieries near Medomsley. The Blackton Mill, at Eggleston, had its own colliery not far away at Whitehouse on Langleydale Common.

Tan Hill collieries, on Stainmore, had served Swaledale smelt mills from the mid-seventeenth century and in fact it was common to the whole North Pennines that the smelt mills all had a fairly local supply of coal and peat. Carriage had been by pack horse, sledge or cart. Women were employed at some smelt mills as 'servers', bringing peat from the stacks or peat house to the furnace house as required.

The willingness of most large smelt mills to buy even small parcels of concentrates made possible the existence of many small independent mines all over the Pennine mining fields.

Carriage

Carriage was an essential part of any mining organization except perhaps the smallest. There were a few mines where the bouse was washed at the mouth of the mines and the concentrates were there sold to dealers or smelters who collected them and took them to the smelt mill. In the greater part of the mining fields the carriage of concentrates from the dressing floors to the smelt mill, often some distance away, was essential. Smelted lead was to be carried from the mill to the merchant, market or place of export and in the reverse direction stores, timber and other supplies were brought to the mines. Fuel from the peat beds on the fells or coal from collieries was also a regular load. In general these journeys were made by a group of men separate from the miners, the carriers, or in the case of larger companies and particularly in the present century by their own teams of carriers or by contractors.

The bulk of carriage in the eighteenth century was done by pack horses which were owned, in strings of twelve to fifteen or more, by men who contracted with the mines for carrying work, either by single journey or by more general arrangement. The Allendale mines and some London Lead Company mines sent lead or concentrates to the Stella Quay on the Tyne, some for the Ryton smelt mill and refinery, and some for Newcastle customers, by the Lead Road which they had made. Many companies owned pack horses which were put out to be maintained at farms and farmers made from this and from carriage a useful supplementary income. In the early part of the nineteenth century the Admiralty, for their Greenwich Hospital Estates in the north, in co-operation with the London Lead Company and the Blackett-Beaumont Company, created a network of new or improved roads which made carriage between the mines, dressing floors and smelt mills in many cases much easier. Carriage of lead from the mills to the customers also eased and the better roads allowed the introduction of new forms of transport, traction engines and mechanical transport of other kinds.

Individual contractors with one horse and cart worked alongside regular employees of the larger companies and pack horses in some places were still working as late as 1880. Only a few photographs have been found of less common forms of transport compared with the almost universal horse and cart, and none have been obtained of pack horses within the area of this book.

Small locomotives of several types were used on narrow gauge tracks between dressing floors and mills and some between mines and dressing floors.

The London Lead Company in 1874 bought a small narrow gauge steam locomotive called 'Samson', which had been designed for them and built by Stephen Lewin at the Poole Foundry, Dorset. Samson ran on a 22 in gauge line between the Cornish Hush Mine and the Whitfield dressing floor in Weardale.

A more orthodox locomotive was one used at Boltsbury, 'The Little Nut', which was built by Hawthorn Leslie of Newcastle upon Tyne.

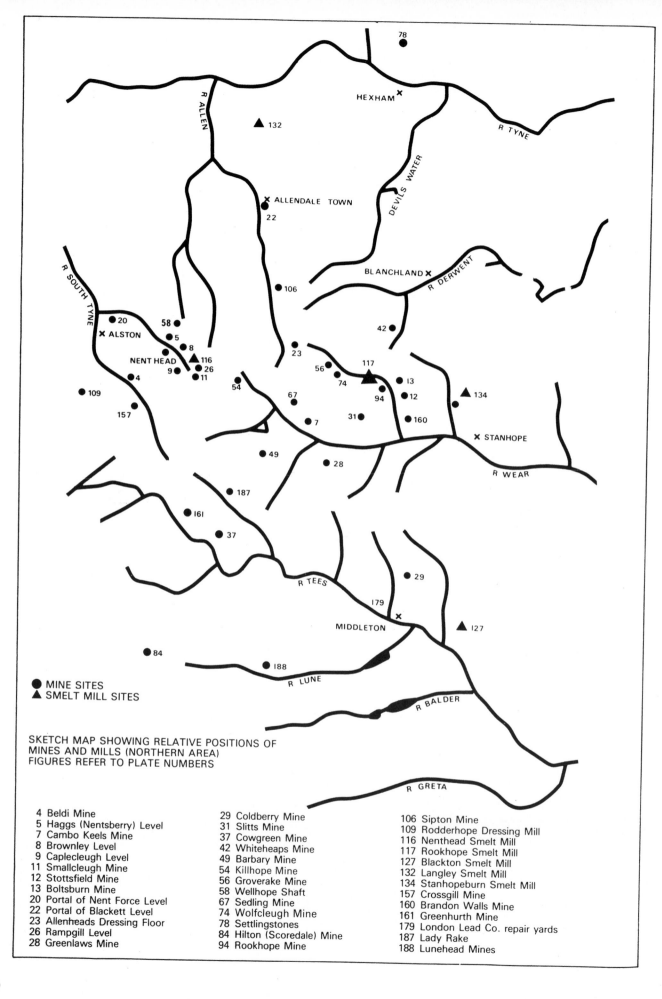

SKETCH MAP SHOWING RELATIVE POSITIONS OF
MINES AND MILLS (NORTHERN AREA)
FIGURES REFER TO PLATE NUMBERS

● MINE SITES
▲ SMELT MILL SITES

4 Beldi Mine	29 Coldberry Mine	106 Sipton Mine
5 Haggs (Nentsberry) Level	31 Slitts Mine	109 Rodderhope Dressing Mill
7 Cambo Keels Mine	37 Cowgreen Mine	116 Nenthead Smelt Mill
8 Brownley Level	42 Whiteheaps Mine	117 Rookhope Smelt Mill
9 Caplecleugh Level	49 Barbary Mine	127 Blackton Smelt Mill
11 Smallcleugh Mine	54 Killhope Mine	132 Langley Smelt Mill
12 Stottsfield Mine	56 Groverake Mine	134 Stanhopeburn Smelt Mill
13 Boltsburn Mine	58 Wellhope Shaft	157 Crossgill Mine
20 Portal of Nent Force Level	67 Sedling Mine	160 Brandon Walls Mine
22 Portal of Blackett Level	74 Wolfcleugh Mine	161 Greenhurth Mine
23 Allenheads Dressing Floor	78 Settlingstones	179 London Lead Co. repair yards
26 Rampgill Level	84 Hilton (Scoredale) Mine	187 Lady Rake
28 Greenlaws Mine	94 Rookhope Mine	188 Lunehead Mines

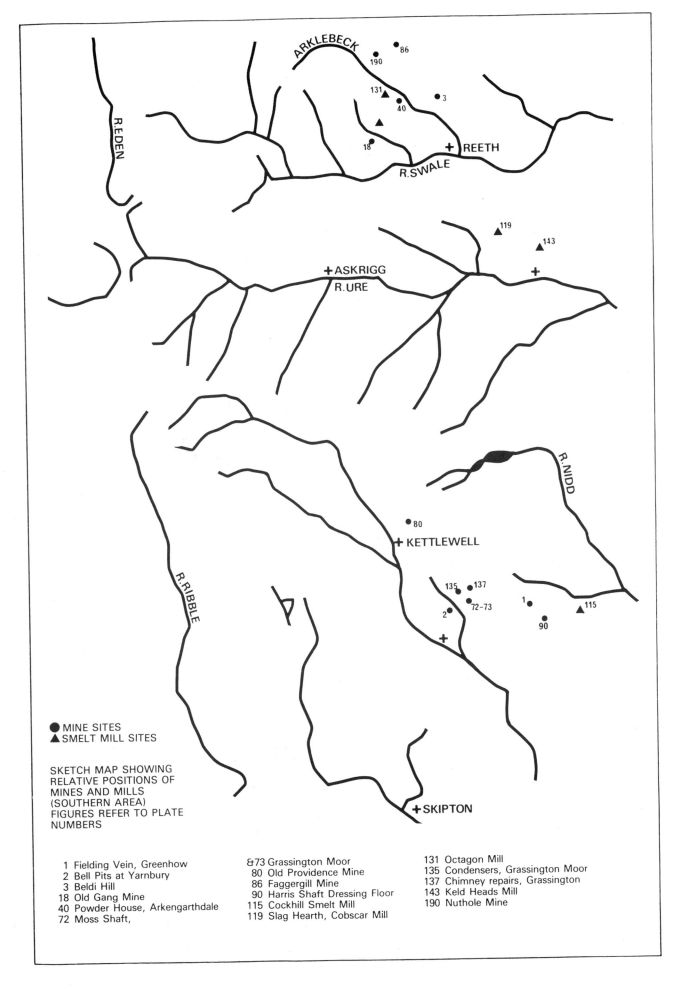

● MINE SITES
▲ SMELT MILL SITES

SKETCH MAP SHOWING
RELATIVE POSITIONS OF
MINES AND MILLS
(SOUTHERN AREA)
FIGURES REFER TO PLATE
NUMBERS

  1 Fielding Vein, Greenhow
  2 Bell Pits at Yarnbury
  3 Beldi Hill
 18 Old Gang Mine
 40 Powder House, Arkengarthdale
 72 Moss Shaft,

&73 Grassington Moor
 80 Old Providence Mine
 86 Faggergill Mine
 90 Harris Shaft Dressing Floor
115 Cockhill Smelt Mill
119 Slag Hearth, Cobscar Mill

131 Octagon Mill
135 Condensers, Grassington Moor
137 Chimney repairs, Grassington
143 Keld Heads Mill
190 Nuthole Mine

11

1. **Opencut working, on the Fielding Vein, Greenhow Hill, North Yorkshire.** This may date back to the sixteenth century, and was probably on one of the leases held by Bolton Priory, near the boundary between Knaresborough Forest and Appletreewick Manor, which were in dispute well into the sixteenth century. Most old opencut workings have been destroyed by later mining activity.   23999

2. **Bell Pits, along the Cockbur Vein, Yarnbury, Grassington, North Yorkshire.** These were first worked in 1603 by miners brought in from Derbyshire by the Earl of Cumberland. This system of working was commonly used in the sixteenth and seventeenth centuries. Shafts were usually about 30 ft deep, but occasionally reached 60 ft. The vein was worked away on each side, as far as was safe and practical with the contemporary methods of ventilation and haulage. At this point, another shaft was sunk further along the vein, its spoil being thrown into the old shaft. This went on, until a line of bell pits marked the course of the vein.

3. **Looking across Gunnerside Gill to the Bunton Mine.** On the hill behind can be seen the tracks of the Old Gang and Bunton Hushes.

4. **Beldi Hill Mine (another), Garrigill, Alston, Cumbria.** This is typical of many small mines. The building near the level mouth is the mine 'shop', which usually housed the miners' changing room and the smithy. It might also contain stables, stores and an office. Some miners lodged in the shop during the week, to save a long walk from a distant home.

18315

5. **Skears Low Level, Hudshope Burn, Teesdale.** This was driven 4,625 ft to Hunt's Coldberry Vein by the London Lead Company in 1821. Many smaller veins were cut, but the mine was only moderately productive. Since 1940, attempts have been made to rework the mine. Mr Mennell, of the Court of the London Lead Company, is seated on the waggon and Mr Korske is leaning against it. Jonathan Hunt, the company's Agent, is on the right of the picture.

14834

6. **Brownley Hill Level.** An old level of the London Lead Company and later a principal level of the Vieille Montagne Zinc Company.

15383

7. **Cambo Keels Mine, Eastgate, Weardale.** This was driven as a horse level by T.W. Beaumont in 1847, but abandoned twenty-four years later. In 1906, the Weardale Lead Company, took the lease, and by 1927 had extracted 30,000 tons of fluorspar. It was reopened again in 1948, and is still working. This photograph shows miners from the latest period of working.

17740

8. **Stope, in Brownley Hill Mine, Nenthead, Cumbria.** Stopes were often extensive; as the height increased, timbers were put in to support working platforms and hoppers. Often, large amounts of 'deads' (waste rock) were left on these platforms, which now poses a serious hazard to explorers, since the timber-work is usually rotten!

9. **Caplecleugh Level, Nenthead.** A narrow roadway cut in solid rock, needing no support; this is an incline, only wide enough to allow the passage of one tub, linking lower workings to the drawing level. The wires are for the electric bells used for signalling between the top and bottom of the incline.

16

10. **Greenside Mine, Helvellyn, Cumbria.** Miners having their break for 'bait' or 'snap', 1904. They are in a wide, unsupported roadway made in good rock. 15364

11. **Stotsfieldburn Mine, Rookhope, Weardale.** A heavily-timbered level. Timber was used to support the roof in many levels, and the mining companies often grew their own in an effort to reduce costs. In 1815, the London Lead Company, enclosed and planted part of the Alston Moor Allotment, to produce timber for the mines. Regular planting began in Teesdale in 1815, and in Priorsdale in 1822. By 1834, 500 acres of Priorsdale was 'of great value' for timber, and 4,220 ft were cut there in 1841. The loco in the picture is being driven by Harry Foster. 23898

12. **Smallcleugh Level, Nenthead.** A small level cut in the solid rock below a worked-out stope. 19220

13. **Boltsburn Mine, Rookhope, Weardale.** Timber in an area of stoping; Tom Maddison, the Manager, is on the right. Many plantations were made in Weardale and the Allendales by the Blackett-Beaumont Company. Both it and the London Lead Company, regularly reported the savings made thereby in the cost of mine timber. 18395

14. **Greenside Mine, Helvellyn, about 1900.** Captain Borlase and three miners in the timbered main level. The wooden chute is delivering rock from a stope above. 15371

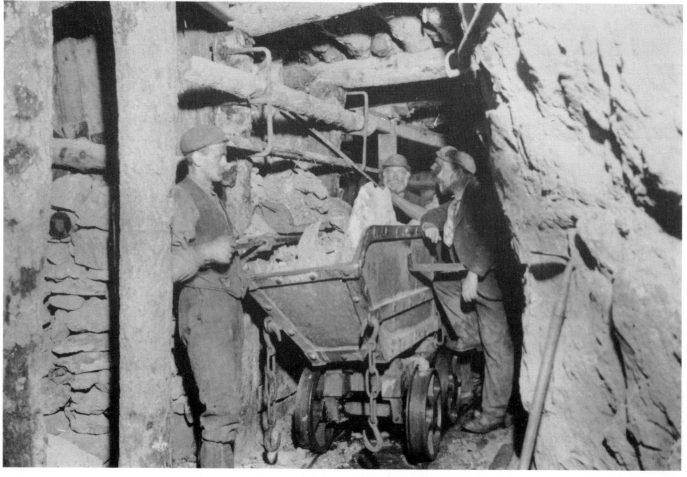

15. **Smallcleugh Level, Nenthead.** Stone arching. Here, it is possible to have solid rock at one side of the level, by driving along the footwall of the vein. Stone arching supports the other side and the roof. In an attempt to reduce maintenance costs, the London Lead Company, ordered, in 1827, that 'all drawing levels, shafts and sumps are now constructed of stone.'

16. **Smallcleugh Level, Nenthead.** Here both sides are in rock and the arch forms the first floor of the stope above. This preserved the drawing level from damage in the event of a failure in the stope timbering. The chute fed bouse (ore) from the stope into waggons. The door helped to regulate the ventilation.

17. **Smallcleugh Level, Nenthead.** In this section of the level, the ground is so broken and unstable that it could only be held by narrow-span arching and careful backing.

18. **Knott Level, Old Gang Mines, Swaledale, North Yorkshire.** An exploration level abandoned short of its intended objective. The arching is built with heavy blocks typical of the Yorkshire Millstone Grit. This is in contrast to the more flaggy rocks of the Yoredale series seen in the photographs of Smallcleugh.

19. **Greenside Mine, Helvellyn.** Fungus growing in a level around the mouth of a chute. Still air and continual damp encourage fungus growth on wood — always a problem in older mines.

15374

20. **Nent Force Level, Alston.** This famous level was intended to drain the mines of the Nent valley, and to explore the ground. Three shafts were sunk on its course, for ventilation and quicker driving. The level rises 210 ft at Haggs Shaft, and terminates at the Brewery Shaft, Nenthead — a total distance of 4.94 miles.

21. **The Nent Force Level.** The entrance to the level seen after the original portal had been destroyed by quarrying. The level was driven as a canal, as far as Haggs Shaft, and at one time visitors were taken, by boat, for more than a mile along the level.

22. **The Blackett Level, Allendale Town, Northumberland.** The entrance to the level. In 1859, Thomas Sopwith, Agent for the Blackett-Beaumont Company, assisted by the engineer T.J. Bewick, started this level which was planned to reach and drain the Allenheads mines. By 1912, when work ceased, $4\frac{1}{2}$ miles had been driven, and three shafts sunk along its length, at Studden Dene, Holmes Linn and Sipton. The level discovered a few veins, some of which made successful mines.   1789

23. **Allenheads, Northumberland.** A view over the village, showing Gin Hill Shaft, with part of the dressing floor and bouse teams on the right. The Pyramidal building over the shaft is similar to those built on all the Blackett Level Shafts; the original drawings used in their construction still survive.
18075

24. **Boltsburn Mine, Rookhope, Weardale.** A group of miners, about 1900. The men are dressed alike; heavy woollen shirt, jacket and waistcoat of good cloth and moleskin trousers. Footwear was usually clogged boots and, by this time, flat caps were commonly worn. Jacket and waistcoat were often removed in the mine working place. All the men carry sticks, to ease the long walk – often over a mile – along the level.
17526

25. **Boltsburn Mine.** A group of miners, some holding candle lamps. Candles were a great expense – provided, but charged for, by the company. In 1815 it was reported to the Court of the London Lead Company, that £225 per annum was being saved by competitive purchasing of candles. At the small mines, men often made their own tallow candles from scrap fat.   15941

26. **Rampgill Level, Nenthend.** A group of miners at the Rampgill 'Shop', holding acetylene hand lamps run off 'carbide'. Calcium carbide was first discovered in 1862, and came into general use for lighting after the adoption of a cheap, American method of production, in the 1890s. Carbide lamps gave about 10 times more light than the candles which they rapidly replaced.

24

27. **Blackdene Mine, West Blackdene, Weardale.** A miner and his pony, both with electric cap lamps. These came into use in the 1940s and gradually replaced carbide lamps. The miner is Mark Allinson. 23899

28. **Greenlaws Mine, Daddry Shield, Weardale.** A Riding Tram. Boards could be placed across the frame to provide seats and the open ends allowed timbers, rails and other materials to be carried into the mine. 18711

29. **Coldberry Mine, Middleton-in-Teesdale.** A tram for timber also used as a 'rider'. The miners are (left to right) Joe Gargett, Tom Allison and Joseph Watson.   16259

30. **Caplecleugh Level, Nenthead.** A 'windy billie'. This is a hand-turned fan, which could be set up in a working place where ventilation was bad. Good ventilation was always a priority and was not always easy to create.

31. **Greenside Mine, Helvellyn.** A view of hand- drilling, with two pairs of drillers. Note the candle stuck onto the rock with a ball of clay, and the scraper for cleaning debris out of the drill holes.   15382

32. **Greenside Mine, Helvellyn.** A pair of hand drillers, in the early twentieth century. The hand drilling technique remained relatively unchanged from the seventeenth century. Two men worked as a team, one holding the drill steel whilst the other struck it with a heavy hammer. The drill was rotated by hand between blows and men would often take turns at the strikers job. The technique was slow and arduous but required very little equipment.   15387

33. **Rodderhope Fell Mine, Alston, Cumbria.** Three pairs of drillers working in a 'flat'. 'Flats' are ore bodies extending laterally from the vein – the rich South Flats at Rodderhope Fell ran for 300 ft to one side of the vein. The entrance to this mine was by means of the Blackburn Level laid out by Smeaton. This ran for 2,900 ft to the Victoria Vein and then a further 1,300 ft to the Main Vein. The mine's extensive workings already included two internal shafts and 5,000 ft of drifts when it was taken over by the Vieille Montagne Zinc Company, in 1907. Amongst other developments, they added a third internal shaft and an incline. The mine closed in 1947. 16586

34. **Boltsburn Mine, Rookhope.** A pair of drillers working at the forehead. In the foreground, two men are working with pick and shovel.

17528

35. **Greenside Mine, Helvellyn.** Dry drilling in a stope. This picture shows an early compressed-air rock drill mounted on a screw-jack stand which the driller's mate would move forward on a ratchet as the hole was drilled. These cumbersome machines increased the speed with which levels could be advanced, but unfortunately produced copious quantities of dust. 15388

36. **Haggs Level, Nentsberry.** Compressed-air drills in use. The first drills of this type to be used in the north were introduced to Swaledale and Allendale in 1864.

15093

37. **An air compressor, at the bottom of the Brewery Shaft, Nenthead.** Water from Smallcleugh Dam and the Perry Dam fell 400 ft from a tower at the top of the Brewery Shaft, dragging air with it, through 'snore holes' in the pipe. At the bottom, the air was released into a receiver, and the water rose 200 ft to an overflow. It then fell once more to the shaft bottom, where it powered two Pelton Wheels, each of which drove a compressor. The compressed air was mainly used to power rock drills. 15385

38. **Cowgreen Mine, Langdon Beck, Teesdale.** Wet drilling in a stope. This modern rock drill has a second hose for water, which is forced down the inside of the drill bit to lay the dust and sluice it out of the hole. Although quite complicated, the drill is lighter and more compact than the early types.

17747

39. **The CB Powder House, Langthwaite, Arkengarthdale, North Yorkshire.** This fine hexagonal building was the central black powder store for the C.B. (Charles Bathurst) Mines, which covered much of Arkengarthdale. It was important to keep powder dry and secure, and it was taken into the mine daily, as required.

40. **Greenside Mine, Helvellyn.** The shot firer. In large mines specially-trained shot firers were in charge of all work with explosives. They inspected the shot holes, charged them and set the fuses. When all the men had been warned and were in a safe place, the shots were fired electrically. The pattern of the holes must be made according to what rock needs to be broken out, which demands great skill and judgement.
15381

31

41. **In the famous Boltsburn Flats** – filling tubs with bouse ready to go out of the mine. At Boltsburn, the flats extended for over 2 miles along the vein and varied in thickness up to 20 ft. They were discovered by the Weardale Lead Company, in 1892, were worked until 1932 and for a time made Boltsburn the richest mine in the north. 18365

42. **A nineteenth-century end-tipping waggon,** made of rivetted wrought iron on a heavy wooden underframe. This waggon came originally from Whiteheaps Mine, Ramshaw, Co. Durham. 'Sets', 'Rakes' or 'Shifts' of 6–8 tubs, were drawn by a horse or, in some later mines, by a locomotive. A 'trammer' was often employed to fill, take out and empty tubs, but in a large mine the drawing might have been let on contract. SR 25/12

43. **Cowgreen Mine.** A modern end-tipping tub made entirely of steel. It is designed for use in the larger, newer levels and has a greater capacity than the 'Whiteheaps' tub shown in the previous photograph. Iron rails were used underground from the early nineteenth century – the London Lead Company, introduced them to all its mines in 1817.   17746

44. **Stotsfieldburn Mine, Rookhope.** Miners using an 'Eimco' rail-mounted, compressed-air rocker-shovel to muck out after blasting the forehead. This photograph shows the operator reversing the machine away from the rock pile and his mate squaring up the tub. Note the shotfiring wire running along the floor.   15272

45. Stotsfieldburn Mine. The 'Eimco' in the process of 'throwing over', where the bucket full of muck is tipped into the tub yoked to the back of the machine. The 'greedy board' prevents spillage of muck during loading.   15271

46. Flushiemere Mine ('The Flush'), Newbiggin-in-Teesdale. Brian Bainbridge, a trammer, with his pony, coming out of the level. The pony's harness includes a heavy leather bridle to protect eyes and face from the rough sides and roof. The leather sheet protects its quarters from water dripping from the mine roof.   18270

47. **Rampgill Level, Nenthead.** Horse drawing a shift of tubs from the mine. On the left, there are some timber or riding trams which have been put off the road. In the days of the Vieille Montagne Zinc Company, Rampgill was the main entrance to an important area of working.

16585

48. **Coldberry Mine, Middleton-in-Teesdale.** William Coltman, a trammer at this small mine. The pony is in 'limber gears', a modified form of carthorse harness, specially developed for working up and down inclines in mines. The 'limbers' (shafts) stay on the pony all day, and can be fixed to either end of any tub. The Coltman family were great horsemen, and raced trotting ponies as well as working in the mines.

17227

49. **Barbary Mine, Ireshopeburn, Weardale.** A pony outside the level mouth, yoked to a tub with trace harness. This very simple form of harness could only be used on the flat. Barbary was once a rich London Lead Company mine. In the nineteenth century, the lease was taken to the Beaumonts, who drove this horse level and worked the mine between 1818 and 1872. It was reopened again in 1905, and produced fluorspar until 1934, employing a few miners, a trammer and the manager.   16534

50. **Brownley Hill Mine, Nenthead.** A trammer and one of the level horses standing outside the mine 'shop'. The trammer is appropriately dressed for working in the wet and draughty levels: sleeved waistcoat, moleskin trousers with 'yorks' and clogged boots.
14941

51. **Cowgreen Mine, Langdon Beck, Teesdale.** Trammers at a passing place on the main level. Reuben Bayles with the pony and Stan Watson, working with modern steel tubs. 15956

52. **Coalcleugh Level, Nenthead.** An early underground locomotive at work. These locomotives were built to a patent design, in Germany, by the Schram Engineering Company, who also made some well-known rockdrills. A number of them were introduced at Nenthead about 1912. 5389

53. **Nenthead.** A Schram locomotive on a shift of tubs near Nenthead Mill. These were steam locomotives using a patent water-tube boiler fired by paraffin. Unfortunately, the fumes proved to be dangerous underground, so the locomotives had to be restricted to outdoor work.

18210

54. **Park Level, Killhope, Weardale.** An early underground locomotive manufactured by the Hydroleum Company. The square section on the left is the patent oil-fired water-tube boiler, the cylindrical tank contained fuel, while water was carried in the centre section. The four small cylinders were mounted horizontally at the front.

16840

55. **Greenside Mine, Helvellyn.** The first electric locomotive to work underground in England was introduced here by Captain Borlase in 1891. It was rated at 30 HP and could pull eighteen tubs. This photograph, taken about 1910, shows the locomotive on the Lucy Level, about to run in bye to the top of the Lucy Shaft.   16383

56. **Grove Rake Mine, Rookhope, Weardale.** This mine was worked by the Beaumont Company, from 1819 to 1883, and thereafter by the Weardale Lead Company, until 1916, and finally closed in 1983.   9309

57. **Grove Rake Mine.** The shaft head and tips. This mine has been worked intermittently by various owners during the twentieth century. The most recent working has been by the British Steel Corporation for fluorspar. 19321

58. **Wellhope Shaft, Nenthead.** This shaft was sunk in 1925 by the Vieille Montagne Zinc Company, to a depth of 416 ft. It entered Haggs Mine near the intersection of the High Raise and Dupont Veins. The shaft made possible the working of a number of outstanding discoveries between the wars. An aerial flight took the bouse to the New Mill at Nenthead. 15543

59. **Boltsburn Mine, Rookhope.** A beam pump, driven by an enclosed waterwheel, seen in use during the widening of the New Shaft, in 1885.
16766

60. **The Wellhope Shaft** was abandoned and the mine was once again served by the Haggs level. The aerial flight had unfortunately been the subject of repeated troubles.

61. **Boltsburn Mine.** On the right of the photograph is the enclosed waterwheel which operated the pumps in the New Shaft. The building on the left housed the steam winding engine.

16767

62. **Boltsburn Mine.** The horse pulled sets of tubs between the New Shaft and the dressing floor.

16109

63. **Boltsburn Mine.** A general view of the mine, showing the headstock, winding engine house and enclosed waterwheel for the New Shaft. The long, single storey building in the centre of the photograph is the school, built and maintained by the company, as was customary in the northern Pennines. 18363

64. **Dene Howl or Healeyfield Mine, Castleside, Consett, Co. Durham.** This photograph shows a fine group of buildings, at the lead mine situated on the edge of the coalfield in north-west Durham. The steam winding engine was in the building at the foot of the chimney, and the tall building to the left of the headstock contained a beam pumping engine. 3116

65. **Breckton Hill Mine, Allendale.** This photograph, taken before 1890, shows a group of buildings which are altogether typical of many northern lead mines. As was usual, the dressing mill was powered by a waterwheel, and the low level of the stream illustrates the summer water shortage which was a common problem: in the winter, the reverse was often the case.   1485

66. **Sipton Mine, Allendale.** A distant view of the mine buildings, illustrating the rural setting of many mines.   9315

67. **Sedling Mine, Cowshill, Weardale.** This mine was worked by the Beaumont Company, between 1818 and 1878; later it was developed as an important fluorspar mine by the Weardale Lead Company, and was finally closed in 1948. The building on the right with the hipped roof contained a large reversible waterwheel which powered the winding drum. To the left of the headstock is the pit for the wheel which drove the pumps for the 425 ft shaft.   19317

68. **Sedling Mine.** The enclosed waterwheel which drove the pumps. The crank and flat rod can be seen in the picture, but the pump bob is enclosed.   16776

69. **Boltsburn Mine.** The cage, at the top of the New Shaft. Tom Maddison, the Manager, is looking on.   18364

70. **Boltsburn Mine.** A group of miners with candle lanterns, standing in front of the cage at the bottom of the shaft.   16835

71. **Greenside Mine, Helvellyn.** The cage at the bottom of the Lucy Shaft. There were three underground shafts at Greenside; the Lucy Shaft, the Willie Shaft and Smith's Shaft. These were originally served by hydraulic winding engines, which Captain Borlase replaced by electric winders, the one on Smith's Shaft being the first installed in a British metal mine. The water that had previously driven the hydraulic engines was then diverted and used to run a hydro-electric generator.   15370

72. **Old Moss Mine, Grassington Moor, Wharfedale.** The remains of a headgear and of the idler pulleys for a rope run, built in the 1850s by John Taylor, the Duke of Devonshire's agent. The shaft was wound from the Brake House Wheel, which was built about 1820, was 52 ft in diameter and could work four shafts at once. Over the years, it served seven different shafts.   24000

73. **Moss (Coalgrovehead) Shaft, Grassington Moor, Wharfedale.** Like Old Moss, this was an old seventeenth century mine reworked during the nineteenth century by John Taylor. This shaft was wound and pumped by the 45 ft diameter wheel in the High Winding House, built about 1865.

16927

74. **Wolfcleugh Mine, Rookhope, Weardale.** An old mine reopened by the Weardale Lead Company, early this century. On the left is the steam-hauled 2 ft gauge railway which ran to the Boltsburn washings. In the background, the faint outline of Grove Rake Mine is visible.

16771

75. **Smallcleugh Mine, Nenthead.** Loading ore from the bouse teams, to go for dressing at Rampgill Mill. The building on the left housed the offices and drying rooms and the one in the centre was the smithy. In the background, a pony pulling a shift of tubs is about to enter the level. 16588

76. **Rampgill Mine, Nenthead.** Loading tip material from the dumps, for dressing. This took place about 1910, some while after the mine itself had closed. 5378

77. **Coldberry Mine, Teesdale.** Hand picking bouse. This is the first stage of ore dressing, where lumps of stone and spar are picked out and discarded, and nuggets and clean ore are collected. The material then remaining goes to be crushed, either by hand or machine, before entering the various separation processes. This photograph was taken in the 1930s, when the tips were being reworked for lead, using the old methods and equipment, by R.W. Raine.   16264

78. **Settlingstones Mine, Corbridge, Northumberland.** The ore travelled along a 'picking belt', on which it was sorted by a succession of men and boys standing beside the moving belt. This was an effective but labour-intensive method of sorting ore.   16396

79. **Rampgill Mine, Nenthead.** A small set of stamps for crushing ore. It is often said that stamps were introduced to the north in 1796 by Richard Trathan, a miner from Cornwall. This, however, cannot be true, since the London Lead Company's account books contain entries for the costs of making and installing stamps at Jeffry's Mill and elsewhere, in December 1737. The accounts also show that waterwheel driven stamps were in use on all its dressing floors shortly afterwards. 16475

80. **Old Providence Mine, Kettlewell, Wharfedale.** A double set of crushing rollers erected in 1863. The iron waterwheel, which was 22 ft in diameter and 4 ft 6 in wide, was directly coupled to one roller. The second roller rode against the first. The weight regulated pressure and thus, to a certain extent, controlled the size of the crushed material. The roller crusher was first introduced to the North in 1816. The Engineer-Manager at Providence, Ralph Place, came from Swaledale where he had seen similar crushers in use. The wheel was partly cut up for scrap in the 1960s but the rollers were saved and taken to the Skipton Museum, with one set on display at the Earby Mines Museum. 20894

81. **Coldberry Mine, Teesdale.** Iron waterwheel with wooden spokes which originally drove both stamps and a roller crusher. The nogs on the wheelshaft, which worked a set of three stamps, can be seen on the right. On the left is the gearwheel which drove the roller crusher.

16242

82. **Coldberry Mine, Teesdale.** Another waterwheel which drove crushing machinery. Here, the rollers have been replaced by a jaw crusher, which crushed the larger lumps – a job previously done manually by boys with spalling hammers.

16251

83. **Boltsburn Dressing Floor.** Bouse was brought in from the levels by the narrow-gauge railway which ran along the gantry on the right of the photograph. Below it can be seen the track which ran to the bouse teams from the head of the New Shaft. Crushers and other machinery were located in the various buildings. Waste went to the tips by way of a railway incline and the aerial flight. 17543

84. **Hilton Mine, Scordale, Appleby, Cumbria.** Two impressive waterwheels. The upper waterwheel powered the crushing plant and the lower one the dressing machinery. At Hilton, there is an ancient opencut more than 1000 ft long, which was succeeded by several levels along its length. These levels were worked by the London Lead Company, between 1824 and 1876, and produced more than 10,000 tons of lead concentrates. The mine was reopened in 1896, for barytes, and finally closed in 1913. This site was popular with explorers for many years, but now forms part of an Army firing range which prohibits access. 16316

85. **Coldberry Mine.** Two hotching tubs. These represent the first stage in the dressing process, and consisted of a square sieve suspended in a tub of water from one end of a long wooden lever. The sieve, containing crushed bouse, was moved rapidly up and down in the water by jerking the lever. The movement of water through the sieve could, with a skilled operator, separate the bouse into layers of ore concentrate, middlings (mixed ore and waste for re-dressing) and waste for the dumps. 16241

86. **Faggergill Mine, Arkengarthdale, North Yorks.** A hotching tub and operator. The principle of the hung sieve was introduced about 1826 by Captain Barrett in the Grassington Mines. Hotching tubs were very simple in design, and could easily be built at a small mine. 16941

87. **Cashwell Mine, Garrigill, Cumbria.** A general view of the mine, 'shop' and the small dressing floor, taken before 1900. The floor contained stamps and hotching tubs, driven by an enclosed waterwheel.   17251

88. **Allenheads Dressing Floor.** The larger mining companies were always keen to improve efficiency, and the Blackett-Beaumont Company, co-operated with the famous Tyneside inventor and industrialist Sir William Armstrong, in the development of a variety of mining equipment. This photograph, taken before 1880, shows four of Armstrong's 'patent improved' hotching tubs. In these, the heavy sieve was counterbalanced and the leverage altered so that greater output could be achieved with no extra effort by the boy who worked the tub. On the gantry over the bouse teams is a patent 'unloader' for the incoming tubs – another Armstrong invention.   17527

89. **Allenheads Dressing Floor after abandonment.** The building with a ramp was the crusher house, the bouse teams were on the left and the slime trunks on the right. The tall building with a pyramidal roof was the cover for Gin Hill Shaft, and was built to the Blackett-Beaumont Company's standard pattern.

15631

90. **North Rake Mine, Greenhow Hill, Yorkshire.** The Harris Shaft Dressing Floor. On the left is a set of early hotching tubs. The boys are hand picking ore, and moving crushed bouse for hotching. The photograph has been carefully posed for artistic effect so the jobs appear confused!

19167

91. **Slitt Mine, Westgate-in-Weardale.** The first stage in dressing bouse. An enclosed waterwheel operated the crushing rollers and, through shafts and gearing, a small bank of mechanical jigs. This jig is basically a mechanized hotching tub, in which the sieve is moved by eccentrics rather than a lever.   19195

92. **Greenside Mine, Helvellyn.** Mechanical jigs were soon improved. The most important change was introduced by Pether-ick in 1831. In his design, the sieve was fixed in one compartment and water was forced through it by a piston operating in a communicating compartment. The loaded sieve no longer had to be lifted, and the energy saved allowed more bouse to be handled in the jig.   16382

93. **Boltsburn Dressing Floor.** A team of girls who came to work on the dressing floor during the Great War, to replace men who had joined the forces. Their clothing and waterproof boots were provided by the company.   12067

94. **Sedling Mine, Cowshill, Weardale.** The 'Washing Master' with his assistant and team of boys. In the early nineteenth century, ore washing or dressing was done by women. In 1828, the London Lead Company, reported that women had been replaced on the dressing floors by boys and that this had resulted in a saving of 150 jobs.   18383

95. **Barbary Mine, Ireshopeburn, Weardale.** An old mine being reworked. Under the watchful eye of the manager, a boy is working at a straight buddle which on a larger dressing floor would follow the hotching tubs. This was a sloping platform with a stream of water running down it fast enough to carry away stone and spar, leaving the galena behind. The feed material was all reduced to a small size and thrown into the stream of water by the operator. 17731

96. **Settlingstones Mine, Haydon Bridge, Northumberland.** A circular buddle. This development of the straight buddle was more efficient and could work automatically. A circular buddle had a conical base; the bouse was fed in as slurry at the raised boss in the centre and flowed out to the circumference. 16395

97. **Settlingstones Mine.** A circular buddle in action. Mechanical stirrers helped the ore to flow evenly downwards. The heavy ore is dropped first, near the centre, and lighter waste outwards and downwards towards the edge.   16403

98. **Greenside Mine, Helvellyn.** In this circular buddle, the slurry was delivered through nozzles fixed at a right angle to the end of the short delivery arms. The nozzles transmitted just enough power to keep the arms moving round, which ensured that the ore was evenly distributed.   16380

99 **Greenside Mine, Helvellyn.** Emptying a buddle. The lead ore would be in a narrow zone near the central boss. The first would result in a concentrate of about 40 per cent ore which was increased to 70 per cent by the second buddling. The outer zone, being dug out in the photograph, contained the waste. In between were the 'middlings' or 'chats' containing 10 per cent – 12 per cent or ore, which were saved and buddled again.

16932

100. **Coldberry Mine.** The dressing floor. The buildings contained a water turbine and a small steam engine to drive the jigs and buddles; the waterwheel drove the crushers: on the left is part of a Lisburn, or impellor, buddle, which was developed in 1827 at Nenthead.

16243

101. **Coldberry Mine.** The Lisburn buddle consisted of a large number of small impellor blades set on a rotating frame. These blades dipped into the bouse in the buddle-stream and moved it steadily uphill against the waterflow. As dressing techniques improved, it often proved to be economically worthwhile to reprocess the wastes from earlier workings – a situation that continues unchanged to this day.

16240

102. **Dene Howl or Healeyfield Mine, Castleside, Consett, Co. Durham.** The dressing mill, showing two large enclosed waterwheels. The upper wheel drove the crushers; the lower drove a row of jigs in the shed and a Lisburn buddle on the left. Waterwheels were enclosed to prevent the wind blowing water out of the buckets, which caused quite a serious loss of power.

8548

103. **Coldberry Mine.** Tom Allinson with a 'Dolly Tub'. This apparatus was widely used for re-treating the finest slimes from the buddles. The slimes were mixed with water in the tub and stirred with a shovel or paddle. Here Tom has lifted out the paddle, before starting to empty the tub. The ore and waste settled differentially with the heavy ore at the bottom. Settling could be assisted by a hard knocking on the side of the tub.   16239

104. **Stanhopeburn Mine, Stanhope, Weardale.** Brunton Cloth Separators. These consisted of a broad belt of specially-made canvas, fitted with wooden slats at 2 ft intervals, which travelled round two rollers. The whole apparatus, which was about 8 ft long, was fixed on a slope. One roller was driven which moved the cloth uphill against the flow of water and slimes. Waste was carried off with the water, whilst the ore remained on the cloth, being carried along and then washed off as the cloth ran through a tank underneath.   16837

105. **Sedling Mine.** Four Brunton cloths. These were invented at Allenheads in 1847 and the London Lead Company, bought the patent rights. Four were soon put to work at Nenthead with another four in Teesdale, and they were soon in use at many London Lead Company dressing floors. They were reputed to save 50 per cent of the labour costs and produce a 5 per cent better concentrate.   16207

106. **Sipton Mine, East Allendale.** The new dressing mill. Hydraulic engines were used at many mines and dressing floors in the Allendales. They ran on high pressure water supplied from hydraulic accumulators, which were filled with water pumped from the river by waterwheel. The tall building with a pyramidal roof houses one of the accumulators for Sipton Mill.   16825

107. **Nenthead.** The New Dressing Mill under construction in 1909. The mill was designed to treat 200 tons of ore in a 12 hour shift. After crushing and picking, the bouse was dealt with by 38 jigs, the slimes from which passed to 48 tables – 22 of these were shaking tables (photograph 112) and there were 10 vanning tables, 16 revolving tables (photograph 113) and a magnetic separator for iron.

5852

108. **Nenthead.** Circular tables being prepared for use, in the Rampgill workshops. In order to cut costs, the mining companies whenever possible manufactured and repaired their own equipment.

5382

109. **Rodderhope Fell Mine, Alston.** The Vieille Montagne Zinc Company's new dressing mill. 15369

110. **Rodderhope Fell Mill.** The first gallery of jigs. 16958

111. **Rodderhope Fell Mill.** Another view of jigs. On the left is Mr Wardrop, the mill manager, with the engineer, Mr Walton, on the right.

15275

112. **Rodderhope Fell Mill.** The Wilfley tables, for reprocessing 'middlings' from the jigs. Material was spread by a diagonal stream of water, as the table was rhythmically shaken. Galena, zinc blende, middlings and waste ran into different bands, and were collected by troughs under the edge.

15384

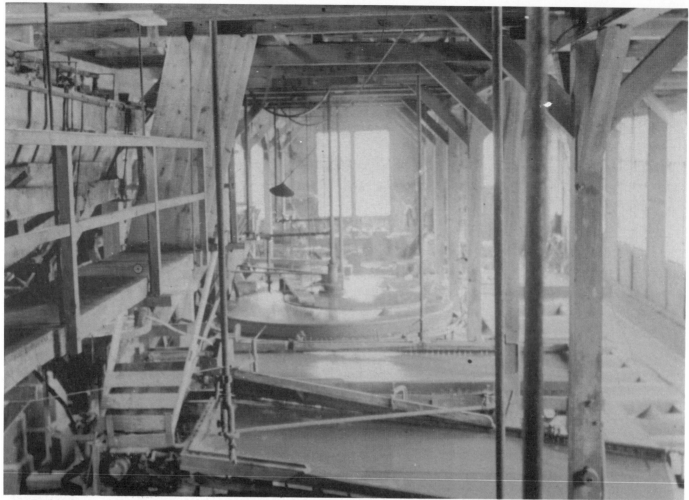

113. **Rodderhope Fell Mill.** Jigs, tables and circular tables. Circular tables were very much like the more old-fashioned circular buddle, being slightly conical and fed with bouse slurry and water from the middle; on rare occasions, they were used dry as picking tables.

16957

114. **Wiregill Mine.** Tom Allinson with the weight scoop used to weigh the dressed ore before sending it to the smelt mill. 16257

115. **Cockhill Smelt Mill, Nidderdale, North Yorkshire.** Records exist of a mill built on this site by Stephen Proctor as far back as 1705, but this early mill was replaced in 1782. There were three partners in the new venture, two of whom at least, the Hutchinsons, had come from the London Lead Company's mines at Alston. The roofless building contained two ore hearths, with the bellows in the building in front. On the right, served by the chimney, is the roasting hearth. The building in the foreground was the blacksmith's shop.

20901

116. **Nenthead Smelt Mill.** A mill was built here in 1738 by the London Lead Company., to treat ore from Rampgill Mine and the royalty ores purchased, untill 1768, from the Trustees of Greenwich Hospital. The mill was later rebuilt with three ore hearths, refining furnaces and a roasting hearth. Although much altered and extended over the years, it remained in use for smelting until the end of mining about 1880. Some years later, the old mill was converted to be an engine and boiler house for the Vieille Montagne Zinc Company's New Mill.

16474

117. **Rookhope Smelt Mill.** Two ore hearths at work. On the right, the workstone and sumpter pot can be seen. In front of each hearth there is an iron pig-mould with two wheels and a leg. At left and right, smelters are pouring molten lead from ladles into the moulds. On the left Bob Oliver and Jack Lowery, on the right Herbert Lowery.   18326

118. **Nenthead Smelt Mill.** A small ore-hearth in the Assay House. This was a scaled-down version of the full size hearths in Nenthead Mill. It was rather like a blacksmiths' hearth blown by waterwheel-powered bellows. In front of the bowled cast-iron hearth is the sloping workstone, with a diagonal channel which took molten lead into the sumpter pot. The lead was then ladled into iron pig-moulds and left to cool.   19171

119. **Cobscar Smelt Mill, Wensleydale, North Yorkshire.** A slag hearth. The grey slag from an ore hearth contained some lead, largely in the form of litharge. This slag could be crushed and re-smelted with coke in a small blast-furnace, which yielded valuable amounts of lead. The process was used in most smelt mills, and produced an easily recognized glassy black slag. This can often be picked up on old smelt-mill sites.   16945

120. **Rookhope Smelt Mill.** A group of smelters, photographed in 1902. The knitted shawls worn by most of the men protected the neck and shoulders from the heat and strong draughts created by the hearths.   16762

121. **Rookhope Smelt Mill.** Tipping the slags. The wheeled slag-ladles had a cranked axle and pivoting post. The piece of wood was used to lever free the slag when it had set.

16823

122. **Nenthead Smelt Mill.** The Assay House, at Rampgill. Assay laboratories were built by the London Lead Company, in 1833, at Nenthead, Stanhope and Middleton, to check the quality of the smelting and refining. In 1834, Professor Finley Weir Johnson, Reader in Chemistry and Mineralogy at Durham University gave a course of lectures at Middleton-in-Teesdale, attended by all the agents and assistants. Later, assayists and assistants were sent to Dr T. Richardson's classes at Newcastle.

16482

123. **A Pattinson Pan, in the collections at Beamish, The North of England Open Air Museum.** These were used for refining silver from the lead. Lead ore from the Northern Pennines contains a small proportion of silver – about 9 oz per ton – and from an early date the London Lead Company, and others had been major silver producers, by the ancient 'cupellation' process. In this method, argentiferous lead was heated in a porous bed made of bone-ash. At a high temperature, the lead oxidized and was absorbed onto the bone-ash, leaving a small mass of pure silver. After 1833, they changed to the new more economic 'crystallization' process developed by H.L. Pattinson, which used these heavy cast-iron pans.

124. **Nenthead Smelt Mill.** A set of Pattinson Pans. Lead was melted in the pans, and then cooled gradually, the temperature in each pan being controlled by a small fire. As the pan cooled, the crystals which formed contained relatively less silver than the rest of the melt, and could be skimmed off with a perforated ladle. The melt was progressively treated in this way until the final result was a large amount of pure lead and a smaller quantity of silver-enriched lead. This was then put through the cupellation process finally to extract the silver.

16379

125. **Hugh Lee Pattinson** was born in Alston in 1796. His first major appointment was in 1825, as Assay Master for the Trustees of the Greenwich Hospital at their Langley Smelt Mill near Hexham. After a few years, he moved to the Beaumont's Blaydon Mill where he perfected his process of separating silver from lead by crystallization. All his life Pattinson had been on friendly terms with the London Lead Company, who in 1836, paid 100 guineas for the right to use his idea. Over the next few years, the 'Pattinson Process' was developed and improved, and put to work in the London Lead Company's mills at Nenthead, Stanhope, Bollihope and Blackton. Other refining processes were invented, but Pattinson's remained the favourite in the North of England.

18988

126. **Rookhope Smelt Mill.** The first mill was built here in 1752, but was replaced some years later. In 1884 the mill was reported as 'antiquated' and 'inefficient' and was once again rebuilt. The new mill had five ore hearths, a slag hearth, a refining hearth and a roasting furnace. The old flue was extended to a length of 2548 yds and condenser chambers were built along its course.

16850

127. **Blackton Smelt Mill, Eggleston, Teesdale.** The London Lead Company's principal smelt mills. The first lease was taken here in 1771 and eventually there were three mills on the site, serving the London Lead Company's mines in all of Teesdale and parts of Weardale. A great deal of experimental work on the reverberatory furnace was done at Blackton, and the new improved furnaces introduced in 1862 resulted in a saving of one sixth on the cost of the fuel. 17215

128. **Blackton Smelt Mill Chimney.** The end of the lead industry in Teesdale saw the abandonment and demolition of many old mills. The fine octagonal Blackton Chimney was demolished in 1932, for its stone. The job was done by Tom Allinson, one of the last lead miners, who reworked Coldberry Mine for some years and is seen in many photographs in this selection. It was a great public occasion, and this picture was published in the local newspaper, the 'Northern Echo'. 16262

129. **Blackton Smelt Mill, during demolition in 1904.** Blackton was the last of the London Lead Company's Mills at Eggleston. It had a capacity of 14,000 bings per annum and was designed by Robert Stagg. When built in 1820, the mill, which included many of Stagg's improvements and ideas, was said to be the best equipped and constructed of its kind. It apparently reduced the London Lead Company's smelting costs by £1,285 a year.

16249

130. **Bollihope Smelt Mill, Frosterley, Weardale.** This site was first leased by the London Lead Company in 1855. Over the years, there were repeated disputes about renewal of the leases and the site boundaries, with both the Beaumont Company, and the Ecclesiastical Commissioners.

16492

131. **The Octagon Smelt Mill, Langthwaite, Arkengarthdale.** This was built by Easterby, Hall and Company, of Newcastle-upon-Tyne, between 1802 and 1804, to replace Old Moulds Smelt Mill; as part of a lease, the company had agreed to build 'a smelting mill of large dimensions' on the waste of Arkengarthdale. The Octagon Mill was itself replaced in 1883 by the New CB Mill nearby, but the building stood until 1944.   19168

132. **Langley Smelt Mills, Haydon Bridge, Northumberland.** These mills were built for the Trustees of the Greenwich Hospital by Smeaton in 1767. Workmen's housing and a second mill, known as Blagill Mill, were later added and the site in time became so large that Sopwith described it as 'having the appearance of a village'. Blagill Mill was leased to the Blagill Company, from an early date; from 1833, Langley Mill was leased to the Hudgill Company, which thereafter purchased royalty ores from the Trustees and smelted them along with the product of its own mines.   15799

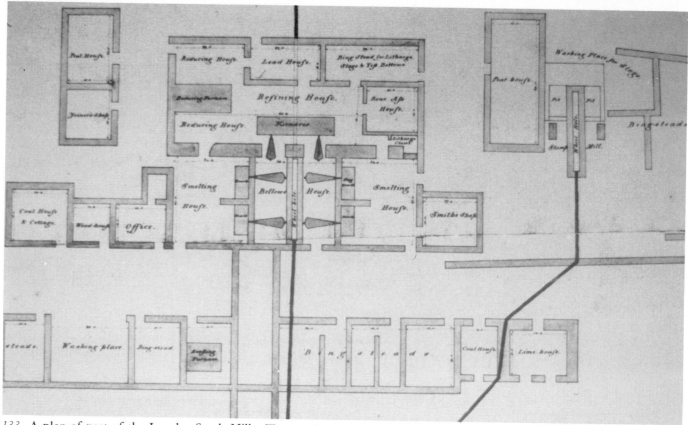

133. **A plan of part of the Langley Smelt Mills.** The complex included refining and reducing furnaces, three orehearths and a slag hearth. There were two waterwheels, which ran the Stamp Mill and ore-hearth bellows. There are stores for peat and coal to run the furnaces and hearths. Peat came from the moors, and coal from the nearby Stublick Colliery.

134. **Stanhopeburn Smelt Mill, Weardale.** This photograph shows the foundations for the flues and condensers and gives some idea of the great length to which flues could run. This was one of the London Lead Company's mills and was originally built in 1806. The condensers were added in 1865, and the flues extended in 1867.

19316

135. **Grassington Cupola Mill, Wharfedale.** This photograph shows two Stokoe condensers on the line of the flue, and the chimney. These were built about 1850, when the whole flue was improved and lengthened.　　16937

136. **Grassington Cupola Mill.** Part of the flues have now been restored. This photograph shows one of the stone dampers, used to isolate extension loops from the flue.

137. **Grassington Cupola Mill.** The chimney under repair by the Earby Mines Research Society. This voluntary group has done much mining history research and restoration in the Yorkshire Dales, and maintains the Earby Mines Museum.

138. **Blackton Smelt Mill, Eggleston, Teesdale.** A group of smelters in the mill yard about 1890. This mill was known for its good working conditions. These particularly included an effective ventilation system, as a result of which the smelters do not need to wear the protective shawls used at Rookhope and elsewhere. Pigs of lead awaiting transport away from the mill are stacked on the right with a few more leaning on end, on the left, all marked 'LEAD COMPANY'.   18710

139. **Weighing of Lead at Richmond Station, North Yorkshire.** After 1848, the lead from some of the Swaledale mills which had been carried to Stockton-on-Tees, went by railway from the North Eastern Railway station at Richmond. In this photograph, taken about 1870, the lead is being weighed on scales before despatch.   16422

140. **Stublick Colliery, Haydon Bridge, Northumberland.** This fine group of nineteenth century colliery buildings, now preserved, once supplied coal to the nearby Langley Smelt Mill. The small area of workable coal measures around Stublick lies on the downthrow side of the Great Stublick Fault, which forms the northern boundary of the North Pennines. Coal from the Main, Stone, Yard, Little and Three-Quarter seams was mined from the early nineteenth century, but most of the workings were abandoned by 1920.   1772

141. **Whitehouse Colliery, Eggleston, Teesdale.** The Eggleston smelt mills supplemented their supply of peat with coal from this mine. Whitehouse Colliery continued to produce coal for the local market for some years after the mills closed. The picture shows a scene very typical of the many small drift mines which once worked the outcropping coal seams in Co. Durham; as such, it offers a marked contrast in appearance with the lead levels seen before. 14461

142. **Rookhope Smelt Mill, Weardale.** This picture shows Jack Lowery, who carted peat to the mill after it had been cut and dried on the moors. Peat cutting was usually done by large family parties. At the Old Gang Mill in Swaledale for example, peat cutting took place during May and June. It involved two dozen carts and over one hundred men, women and children, who cut and carried a year's supply for the mill. 18712

143. **Keld Heads Smelt Mill, Leyburn, Wensleydale.** The peathouse near the mill. This is preserved in good condition but is now used as farm buildings. At many mills, women were employed to carry peat from the peathouse into the mill as required. Large peathouses are not often found in the North Pennines, but every mill had space to store the coal which ensured a constant supply of fuel to run the furnaces and hearths.

144. **Winter on the Leadway, Allendale.** In the early days before 1800, lead was generally carried by pack-horses. These were strong stocky animals of about 14 hh, known as 'Galloways' or 'Gals'. A pig of lead weighed about 1 cwt and one pig was slung in a heavy leather saddlebag on each side of the saddle. The pack-saddles were made of wood reinforced with iron; the collections at BEAMISH include the last two remaining examples, both sadly incomplete.

145. **Saddle House, on the road between Blackton and Eggleston.** Wear on the pack-harness must have been heavy and this shop was one of many built on the busiest routes, to provide shelter where spare saddles could be kept, repairs made or the train halted overnight. Tracks were often almost impassible in winter: in an effort to improve transport, the London Lead Company and the Trustees of the Greenwich Hospital took advice from the great road engineer Macadam, and laid out a network of roads.   18284

146. **Carters, near Boltsburn Mine, Weardale.** After 1805, the 'gals' were gradually replaced by one-horse carts though a few pack horses remained in use as late as 1880. William Cobbett rode from Carlisle to Newcastle in 1832 and says, in 'Rural Rides': 'There are great lead mines not far from Hexham and I saw a great number of little one-horse carts bringing down the pigs of lead to the . . . . Tyne.' This picture shows similar heavily-built 'little carts' nearly a century later, when they were used to carry concentrates from the dressing floor to the smelt mill and pig-lead to the railway.   17542

147 **Cowgreen Mine, Teesdale.** A team of carriers in 1912. On some of the more hilly roads, the carriers would sometimes travel in pairs or even in larger groups. On bad hills, one horse could be unyoked and used as a 'trace horse' to help pull the load uphill.

16071

148. **Lady Rake Mine, Harwood, Teesdale.** J.T. Emerson and T.G. Currah with a load of concentrates for the smelt mill, in 1907. They are driving their Saunderson Tractor. This unusual design, patented in 1907, had three wheels, all of which were driven from the petrol engine.

16072

149. **Nenthead.** A road locomotive used to haul lead from Nenthead smelt mill to the railway at Alston. The picture was taken about 1910 and the locomotive is a B6 'Big Lion' type built by John Fowler and Company (Leeds) Ltd. The design and gearing of these locomotives made them particularly suitable for work on the hilly roads of the Northern Pennines.   18268

150. **Hilton Mine, Scordale, Cumbria.** A road locomotive which hauled concentrates from the dressing mill to the railway at Appleby. After a long life with the London Lead Company and a period of closure, this mine was reopened for barytes in 1896. Later, it was worked for barytes and witherite before finally closing in 1919.   16315

151. **Boltsburn, Weardale.** The Boltsburn mine and dressing floor were served by a 2 ft gauge railway system which was used to transport ore concentrates and stores. This picture shows one of the steam locomotives, Boltsburn No. 2, nicknamed 'The Little Nut', which was built in 1913 by the Newcastle-on-Tyne firm of Hawthorn Leslie & Company Ltd. The men are, left to right, Bill Pattison, William Hogarth, William Ward and Alf Foster, the driver.   18389

152. **Boltsburn, Weardale.** The locomotive Boltsburn No. 2 'The Little Nut' remained in service for many years, but not without some alterations! These small Hawthorn Leslie locos, with their open cabs, were mainly intended for use in the colonies on sugar plantations, etc. At Boltsburn, 'The Little Nut' was soon rebuilt with an enclosed cab, to cope with the wild weather of the Northern Pennines. Its regular crew were Alf Foster and Bill Pattison.   17759

153. **Cornish Hush, Frosterley, Weardale.** This 1 ft 10 in gauge locomotive called 'Sampson' ran between Cornish Hush and the Whitfield Brow dressing floors – part of the London Lead Company's Bollihope development. The locomotive was built for the company in 1847 by Stephen Lewin at the Poole Foundry, Dorset. It had two cylinders and was rated at 3 n.h.p. Lewin was better known for his portable engines, but did build a number of railway locomotives for industrial use. The only surviving example is now at BEAMISH, and came from Seaham Harbour where it first worked in the 1860s.

14836

154. **Rookhope.** A general view of a leadmining village. Boltsburn Mine can be seen at bottom left. Nearby is the railhead for the line running down the valley, and the rope-hauled railway incline up to Bolts Law can be seen, bisecting the picture.

15942

155. **Boltsburn.** The Weardale Lead Company built an aerial flight to take fluorspar from Boltsburn Washings to the North Eastern Railway at Eastgate. This picture shows the loading station for the flight. 16579

156. **Eastgate, Weardale.** The terminal of the aerial flight from Boltsburn, showing a railway waggon being loaded. The sloping structure on the left is the cable tensioner. This flight was designed by Alvin Hill. 16822

157. **Crossgill Mill, Garrigill, Cumbria.** The main power for many mines, dressing floors and mills was a waterwheel. The wheel at this little mill was overshot and was built of iron plate; it was typical of many wheels in the Northern Pennines. At one time, this mill produced lead-covered fuse for the mines. 18294

158. **Crossgill Mill.** This picture shows the sluice which regulated the flow of water onto the wheel – the more water, the faster the wheel turned. The peg holes in the sluice gate handle allowed the gate to be raised and lowered as required. The wheel itself can just be seen in the background. The man is Will Hardman. 18292

159. **Boltsburn Mine, Weardale.** This fine wheel has now been dismantled for scrap, but once provided power for the mine. It was made in Aberystwyth and originally worked on a Welsh mine; it was not unknown for large items of plant to be moved considerable distances from one mine to another.

106

160. **Brandon Walls Mine, Rookhope, Weardale.** A large overshot waterwheel which drove pumps in the shaft, through flat rods. The lead from this mine contained 6 oz of silver per ton, the recovery of which made the mine prosperous. The picture also shows the very fine lime kilns built nearby.

12114

161. **Greenhurth Mine, Nr Low Green, Teesdale.** This backshot wheel was located 500 yds away from Swan's Shaft, so that it could make use of water which had already served the dressing floors. It drove a set of pumps through flat rods from the wheel crank; the bob weight is a counter-balance for the rods. This mine was worked from 1868 to 1902, when it was flooded out. The ore was unusually rich in silver, reaching 12 oz per ton of lead.   17735

162. **Killhope, Weardale.** The dressing mill for Park Level, seen in 1924. The iron waterwheel drove ore preparation machinery inside the mill. In the 1970s Killhope came under the care of Durham County Council, which has repaired the fabric of the mill and opened the site to the public.

163. **Nenthead New Mill, 1912.** These two German-made semi-portable engines were a type usually known as 'Locomobiles'. The engine was mounted on top of its boiler, forming a compact and economical unit. 18877

164. **Nenthead New Mill.** Another source of power in the mill was this large Ruston oil engine. The man is Amos Treloar, the Vieille Montagne Zinc Company's manager at Nenthead. 15386

165. **Jonathon Hunt, Agent of the London Lead Company and his wife, brother, son and two daughters**. This picture was taken at the Company's offices in Middleton-in-Teesdale.

16796

166. **Three outstanding mining consultants**. On the left is Henry Louis, Milburn Professor of Mining at Armstrong College, Newcastle upon Tyne. Next to him is Mr Willis, manager of the Weardale Lead Company, previously with the London Lead Company and for a time manager of the Medomsley Colliery near Consett. On the right is Captain Anthony Wilson, consultant to the Greenside Mines and manager of the Thornthwaite and Threlkeld Mines, Cumbria.

16204

167. **Near Nenthead, 1925.** Selecting and marking out the site for the new Wellhope Shaft. The group of Vieille Montagne Zinc Company. staff includes, left to right: Fred Ridley, engineer; Percy Blight, surveyor; Amos Treloar, manager; George Ward, joiner and Lancelot Liverick, underground foreman.   15092

168. **Boltsburn Mine.** Tom Maddison, the manager, with the assay chemist Jim Pentland.   18394

169. **Threlkeld Mine, Cumbria.** Captain Anthony Wilson, owner-manager of Threlkeld Lead Mines Ltd, at the mouth of a level. The picture was taken in 1913 following an inspection visit, and shows Captain Wilson with George Hewitson and one of the miners. 16530

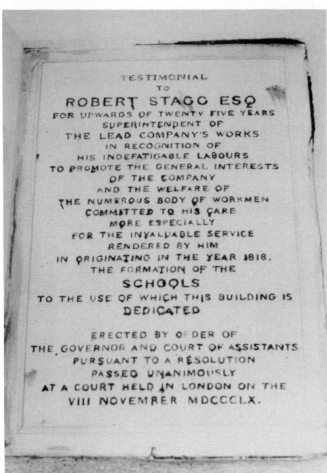

TESTIMONIAL
TO
ROBERT STAGG ESQ
FOR UPWARDS OF TWENTY FIVE YEARS
SUPERINTENDENT OF
THE LEAD COMPANY'S WORKS
IN RECOGNITION OF
HIS INDEFATIGABLE LABOURS
TO PROMOTE THE GENERAL INTERESTS
OF THE COMPANY
AND THE WELFARE OF
THE NUMEROUS BODY OF WORKMEN
COMMITTED TO HIS CARE
MORE ESPECIALLY
FOR THE INVALUABLE SERVICE
RENDERED BY HIM
IN ORIGINATING IN THE YEAR 1818,
THE FORMATION OF THE
SCHOOLS
TO THE USE OF WHICH THIS BUILDING IS
DEDICATED

ERECTED BY ORDER OF
THE GOVERNOR AND COURT OF ASSISTANTS
PURSUANT TO A RESOLUTION
PASSED UNANIMOUSLY
AT A COURT HELD IN LONDON ON THE
VIII NOVEMBER MDCCCLX.

170. **Memorial to Robert Stagg, Agent of the London Lead Company for their mines and estates.** Stagg was born at Middleton-in-Teesdale in 1781. For some years he was Superintendant of Smelting and was then appointed as Agent. He designed the new Egglestone Smelt Mill and developed many significant improvements to smelting techniques; he also had a considerable influence on the social and housing conditions of the miners. This plaque was erected in the new school houses at Middleton in 1861, and Stagg died at Dishforth, Yorkshire on 27 March 1864. 5392

171. **Lodge Syke Mine, Ireshopeburn, Weardale.** Arthur Maddison, a mining surveyor with a vernier theodolite at the shaft head. This is very much a twentieth-century scene: earlier surveyors – 'diallers' – used the 'dial', which is a simple magnetic needle. Careful and accurate surveys were necessary for the proper location of veins, the safe driving of workings and for the production of working plans and sections.   17295

172. **Tom Allinson, one of the last real Teesdale lead miners.** He was an independent miner who took the lease of the old Coldberry Mine during the 1930s, and did a little work underground. Most of his energy was spent in dressing up large amounts of bouse using the old equipment – hotching tubs, buddles and dolly tubs, as already illustrated. This picture shows him with his 'pillow bag' which contained a week's supply of food for his stay in the mine shop.   16233

173. **The interior of an unknown mine lodging shop, early this century.** It is probably evening, and the miners are resting, chatting and passing the time; clothes are drying on the high racks. Most men had a hobby – anything from wood carving to knitting. Communal entertainment often centred around the local songs and tunes, and some miners were capable players of instruments like the concertina or fiddle.   18911

174. **Manor Gill Shop, Middleton Common.** In 1818, the London Lead Company., built lodging shops at some of its remote mines. These were substantial buildings near the mine mouth and were fitted out with bunkbeds, a cooking range and provision for drying clothes. A miner could walk to work on Monday, live in the shop in relative comfort during the week and walk home on Saturday, for the weekend. At those mines where the men did not need to lodge, 'changing shops' were provided, with facilities for drying clothes overnight.   16254

175. **Tom Allison.** An old miner who, helped by his two sons, took the drawing contract at Wiregill and other mines. 16536

176. **Nentsberry, Alston, Cumbria.** Stephen Stout, who worked in Haggs Mine, with his fine family. 14948

177. **Rookhope.** Harry Elliot, a miner at Boltsburn, and his family. The youngest son Arthur, seated in front, grew up to become manager of Blackdene Mine, Weardale.

18416

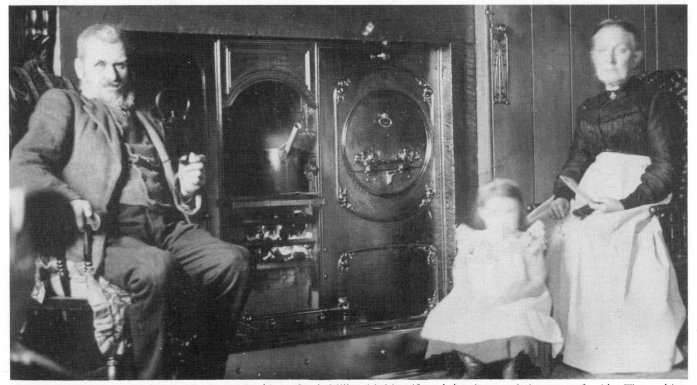

178. **Rookhope.** Tom Gardiner, a smelter at Rookhope Smelt Mill, with his wife and daughter at their cottage fireside. The cooking range with its round oven is an interesting local feature. Round ovens were common in Co. Durham and South Northumberland, but are virtually unknown elsewhere.

5590

179. **Part of the Middleton-in-Teesdale repair yard.** The staff included engineers and wheelwrights and parts of engines and other machinery lie about. The old man sitting at the front is Mark Pinkney, the Chief Engineer, who was responsible for many mechanical improvements to the machinery. He was one of a family with several generations of service with the London Lead Company.   14835

180. **The London Lead Company's repair yard at Middleton-in-Teesdale.** These were the central workshops for the Company's mines and estates in the area. They undertook repair and manufacturing work which called for particular skills or machinery, or where bulk production could bring real cost-savings. This picture shows the part of the workshops where mine wagons were made and repaired.

14838

181. **Ireshopeburn, Weardale.** Carpenters and wheelwrights at the Weardale Lead Company's repair shop.   16142

182. **Middleton House, Middleton-in-Teesdale.** This was the house of the London Lead Company's Agent for Teesdale and Weardale. The house and offices were designed by the architect Bonomi and completed in 1819. Nearby, there were houses for some of the officials, and Masterman Place – the estate – included stables, timber yard and stores.   15002

183. **The Clock Tower, Middleton-in-Teesdale.** This square tower was built over the entrance to the London Lead Company's stables in 1823. A public clock had earlier been erected at Nenthead and had proved so useful that the Company decided to build this one at Middleton. 8120

184. **Smallcleugh Level, Nenthead.** The miners are gathered outside the level mouth, before going on shift. This and the next photograph were taken about 1897, when the mine was being worked by the Vieille Montagne Zinc Company. 17619

185. **Smallcleugh Level.** Another view of the workforce: the number of men employed gives a good idea of the great complex of workings to which this level gives access. The pile of stones in the foreground is for the fine stone arching on the main levels (see photographs 15, 16, 17), which always had to be maintained in good condition.   5380

186. **Nenthead.** A group of Italian miners, about 1900. The Vieille Montagne Zinc Company had mines in Italy and brought some workmen from there to the Northern Pennines. There was, in the end, a multi-national workforce at Nenthead and the entrance to Rampgill Level bore notices in a number of languages.   15642

187. **Lady Rake Mine.** A group of miners, about 1900. This was an old London Lead Company mine, but was never of more than moderate value. The lease was surrendered in 1902, but the mine was reopened in 1904 and worked for a few years by a group of local independent miners.   16551

188. **Lunehead Mine, Lunedale.** A typical group of miners in their working clothes. These follow the usual pattern for miners at the turn of the century – cloth cap, jacket and waistcoat, long trousers and clogged boots. Their walking sticks indicate the long levels to be walked to get to their work places. The woman in the middle of the group used to make sacks for carrying barytes.   15161

189. **Sedling Mine, Cowshill, Weardale.** A group of miners at the drawing shaft.

15644

190. **Nut Hole Mine, Faggergill, Arkengarthdale, North Yorkshire.** Miners near the dressing floor. this was one of an old group of mines reopened in 1908 by the Stang and Cleasby Company. The incline brought bouse up the side of a valley to the level of the dressing floor which served several small mines.

15331A

106

191. **Rookhope, Weardale.** A gang of miners building a new reservoir. The large mining workforce would always be called upon for major 'surface' projects such as this.
16111

192. **Nenthead.** The parade held to celebrate Queen Victoria's Diamond Jubilee in 1897. At the head of the procession are the children of the village and the Nenthead Band. They are walking past the Methodist Chapel and the Reading Room and Library, both of which were built by the London Lead Company.
18212

193. **Nenthead.** The parade for Edward VII's Coronation in 1902, again led by the Nenthead Band. The building is the Vieille Montagne Zinc Company's old dressing mill. In the background, a shift of waggons full of bouse is coming down from Rampgill Mine: the real work continued, even at a time of celebration.   16384

194. **A moment of light relief.** Two miners, Ted Adamson and Bob Gardiner, on an outing to Scarborough in the 1920s. Bob was a miner at Boltsburn and Ted went on to become the owner-manager of Whiteheaps Mine.   19196

195. **The Rookhope Saxhorn Band.** A 'Saxhorn' is a brass instrument somewhat like a trumpet, invented in 1840 by Belgian, Charles Joseph Sax. It was soon taken up by the Stanhope Band, and its distinctive tone quickly became popular with bands in all the mining dales.

12093

196. **The Old Weardale Miners' Band.** An exceptional early photograph taken at the Travellers Rest, Lanehead, in 1866. Starting in the early nineteenth century, bands were formed in all the dales from the Aire to the Tyne, and the tradition lives on today. Back row: Wm. English, M. English, T. Pearson, J. Emerson, J. Pendon, T. Emerson. Front row: John Watson, J. Hodgson, Joe Graham, W. James, W. Featherstone, John English, Jos Peart (Snr).

17538

197. **The Middleton-in-Teesdale Prize Silver Band,** in the former London Lead Company repair yard at Middleton, September 1907. From 1835 it was the London Lead Company's practice to encourage and subsidize the formation of bands and to help with the cost of instruments. Starting in 1860, annual grants of £10 went to the bands at Middleton and Nenthead, amongst others. 17148

198. **The Grassington Miners' Band, about 1870.** Another early band photograph, this time from Yorkshire. The bandsmen's uniform of bowler and button-sprinkled coat is unusual and effective. The men are left to right: Jim Holmes, Sam Parker, Wilson Salkell, William Latham, Tom Ashton, William Gill, Fred Waddilove, Charlie Simpson, John Bake, James Simpson, Jos Brown and Mose Nelson, with Bob Simpson sitting in front.

199. **Tom Maddison and Willie Fairlam, two Weardale miners, at the entrance to a copper mine in Rhodesia.** The little oil lamps and the natives' bare feet must have seemed very strange! In time these two men returned to work in their native dale; but, as the mining industry contracted and offered fewer opportunities for enterprise, many men took their skills abroad to the new mining areas developing in America, Africa and throughout the Empire. In this way, they continued the tradition of those who, a generation earlier, had come from Cornwall, Wales and elsewhere to develop mines in the Northern Pennines. 18366

200. **The Farewell.** A Weardale mining family seen just before emigrating. The sudden fall in the price of lead over the years 1880–82 caused a recession from which the lead mines never recovered: many mines closed permanently. Comparison between the census returns for 1871 and 1891 reveals a decline of 40 per cent to 50 per cent in the population of the Northern Pennines, except in the places where the London and Weardale Lead Companies managed to keep mines open. There was work for some, in the coalfields of Durham and Yorkshire but many families, in despair, were forced to emigrate. The great time of the Northern Lead Miner was over. 15295

INDEX

PHOTOGRAPHIC ACKNOWLEDGEMENTS

The authors and publishers would like to acknowledge with thanks the following people, who collected and loaned the originals of old photographs or have granted permission for the use of copyright material.

Atkinson F., 60 67
Barker L.J., 190
Batey G., 12
Bird R.H., 9 15 16 17 22 30
Broadbent J., 81 82 85 101 103 127 172
Clue J., 107
Darlington & Stockton Times, 100
Dixon R., 88
Foster Alf, 11 83 94 152
Gill M.C., 1, 72
Hackett R., 36 49 58 95 110 113 164 167
Hill Alvin, 68 111 104 105 106 151 166 168
Hill C., 92
McNeil J.H., 3 8
Northern Echo, 34 54
Northern Mine Research Society, 72
Parker H.M., 20
Raistrick A., 2 3 14 18 39 55 73 79 80 86 90 98 99 109 110 111 112 113 115 116 118 122 124 131 135 136 137 143 162 182 198
Roberts A., 27
Robinson J., 59 61 62 120 153 160
Sinclair I., 161 197
Watson A., 24 25 126
Woodhall F., 119 134

All the photographs in this book are covered by copyright or reproduction rights and may not be reproduced without permission. Most of the captions end with a number which refers to a negative in the photographic archive at BEAMISH, The North of England Open Air Museum.
Copy prints from these negatives can normally be purchased by writing, quoting the relevant numbers, to:

The Photographic Archive,
BEAMISH,
The North of England Open Air Museum,
Beamish,
Co. Durham,
DH9 0RG
Tel: Stanley (0207) 231811

BEAMISH The North of England Open Air Museum gratefully acknowledges the generosity of Arthur Roberts, who has donated his royalties from this publication to be used for the benefit of the Beamish Photograph Library. BEAMISH is greatly indebted to Arthur who collected most of the leadmining photographs illustrated in this book. His tireless energy and dedication are an inspiration to us all.